ST(P) MATHEMATICS 1A
Teacher's Notes and Answe

ST(P) MATHEMATICS series:

ST(P) 1A
ST(P) 1B
ST(P) 1A Teacher's Notes and Answers
ST(P) 1B Teacher's Notes and Answers

ST(P) 2A
ST(P) 2B
ST(P) 2A Teacher's Notes and Answers
ST(P) 2B Teacher's Notes and Answers

ST(P) 3A
ST(P) 3B
ST(P) 3A Teacher's Notes and Answers
ST(P) 3B Teacher's Notes and Answers

ST(P) 4A
ST(P) 4B
ST(P) 4A Teacher's Notes and Answers
ST(P) 4B Teacher's Notes and Answers

ST(P) 5A (with answers)
ST(P) 5B (with answers)

ST(P) 5C
ST(P) 5C Copy Masters
ST(P) 5C Teacher's Notes and Answers

ST(P) Resource Book

ST(P) Workbooks:
Drawing and Using Curved Graphs
Measuring Instruments
Symmetry and Transformation
Straight Line Graphs

ST(P) MATHEMATICS 1A

Teacher's Notes and Answers

L. Bostock, B.Sc.

S. Chandler, B.Sc.

A. Shepherd, B.Sc.

E. Smith, M.Sc.

Stanley Thornes (Publishers) Ltd

First published 1984 by
Stanley Thornes (Publishers) Ltd
Old Station Drive
Leckhampton
CHELTENHAM GL53 0DN

Reprinted 1986
Reprinted 1987
Reprinted 1988
Reprinted 1990
Second edition 1991
Reprinted 1992

British Library Cataloguing in Publication Data
ST(P) mathematics 1A. 2nd ed.
   Teacher's Notes and Answers
   1. Mathematics
   I. Bostock, L.
   510

ISBN 0-7487-0541-4

Typeset by Cotswold Typesetting Ltd, Gloucester
Printed and bound in Great Britain by Ebenezer Baylis and Son Ltd,
The Trinity Press, Worcester, and London.

INTRODUCTION

Book 1A is the first of a course of five A books in the ST(P) graded series in mathematics and attempts to satisfy the needs of pupils progressing through the National Curriculum. The A series aims to prepare pupils to achieve about Level 7/8 at Key Stage 3 and the highest level at GCSE.

A number of topics have been introduced as a result of the National Curriculum. Originally featured in the Supplementary Booklet, they have now been incorporated in this new edition. One chapter, Sets, has been removed.

The work in Book 1A covers most attainment targets at Levels 4 and 5, about half at Level 6, some at Level 7 and a few at Level 8. This offers flexibility in the use of the book. For example, the work at Levels 4 and 5 can be used sparingly for consolidation and revision for those pupils who have reached those levels before entering secondary school and there is plenty of work beyond Level 5 to enable them to progress. For pupils who have not reached these levels, Chapters 18 to 21 can be omitted as they are covered again in later books.

The books are intended to be used as reference books by the children. The text is brief and aims to supply explanation for those pupils who wish to remind themselves of the reasons for what they are doing but in most cases does not supply a complete introduction to a new topic, thereby allowing teachers to use their own techniques for developing the understanding and use of mathematics in everyday life.

There is a plentiful supply of carefully graded exercises. Questions that are underlined, e.g. **12**, are extra, but not harder, questions for extra practice or later revision. Questions that are double underlined, e.g. **12**, are for those pupils who manage the straightforward questions easily and require more stretching. Most chapters end with mixed exercises. These can be used as and when the teacher thinks fit.

There are in general no instructions on the use of calculators. Being able to do mental calculations is important and, at this stage a calculator should be used mainly as a check on the pupil's own working. If this book is being used with below average ability children, then they should be allowed to use calculators much more freely because without their help they will remain trapped by the arithmetic and be unable to progress to problem solving. For all pupils, it is important that they should make simple estimates as checks on their working and that they should always ask themselves if their answer is sensible. There should be no excuse for outrageously wrong answers.

Most children need constant reminders of the ordinary processes of arithmetic. Understanding the processes does not automatically lead to remembering how to use them. These are skills that take time to acquire and need plenty of reinforcement. For example, each time multiplication of decimals is involved, they should be reminded how to do it. Mental and oral work also plays a part in reinforcing arithmetic skills; sets of graded tests are provided in the ST(P) Mathematics Resource Book. The Resource Book also provides some ideas for investigational work.

The detailed notes that follow are intended only as suggestions. Teachers will have their own ideas on approach and order of contents. They will also know their pupils well enough to know what they can and cannot tackle.

NOTES AND ANSWERS

The book starts with a large section on arithmetic. This has been kept together because we feel that all children starting a new school with a new teacher benefit from a thorough revision of basic arithmetic. Many children arrive at secondary school not sure of what they do or do not know, and what they do know is often obscured by the use of unfamiliar words.

However, many teachers will want to break up the arithmetic with other work. Tables and Networks (Chapter 13) is particularly suitable for this purpose. It is self-contained and can easily be divided into two sections that can be taught at different times. Symmetry (Chapter 10) is another self-contained unit that can be taught at an earlier stage.

CHAPTER 1   Addition and Subtraction of Whole Numbers

This chapter is intended to give practice in addition and subtraction of whole numbers. We have not introduced the calculator until near the end of this chapter but an earlier introduction may be felt to be appropriate; it can be used to check answers.

EXERCISE 1a (p. 1) Can be used for discussion, e.g. other methods of adding several numbers such as looking for pairs of numbers that add up to ten; can also be used for mental arithmetic.

1. 10	**6.** 24	**11.** 15	**16.** 18
2. 11	**7.** 24	**12.** 17	**17.** 25
3. 14	**8.** 19	**13.** 27	**18.** 32
4. 15	**9.** 20	**14.** 27	**19.** 39
5. 17	**10.** 27	**15.** 33	**20.** 32

21. 24	**22.** 17	**23.** 20	**24.** 33	**25.** 30
26. 21	**27.** 21	**28.** 19	**29.** 26	**30.** 32
31. 26	**32.** 26	**33.** 40	**34.** 37	**35.** 39

EXERCISE 1b (p. 2)

1. 79	**2.** 97	**3.** 65	**4.** 308	**5.** 259
6. 399	**7.** 882	**8.** 2039	**9.** 991	**10.** 2292
11. 549	**12.** 1835	**13.** 9072	**14.** 21 829	**15.** 16 244

16. 112	**21.** 183
17. 158	**22.** 177
18. 242	**23.** 202
19. 797	**24.** 1252
20. 1966	**25.** 2783

1

26. 2062	**31.** 1693	**36.** 581	**41.** 2892
27. 1267	**32.** 1382	**37.** 509	**42.** 6779
28. 2764	**33.** 1896	**38.** 857	**43.** 2226
29. 5936	**34.** 5230	**39.** 1087	**44.** 3569
30. 7525	**35.** 4095	**40.** 1832	**45.** 11932

EXERCISE 1c
(p. 3)

Confidence in problem solving comes from getting the answer right. More able children can be asked for some form of explanation, at least writing the answer in sentence form. Some worked examples will be necessary to indicate what they are expected to write down.

1. 89 p

2. 69 p

3. 88

4. £757

5. a) 261   b) 302   c) 3056   d) 1300

6. a) three hundred and twenty-four
   b) five thousand two hundred and eight
   c) one hundred and fifty
   d) one thousand five hundred

7. 787

8. 77 cm

9. £16

10. 50 min

11. 4957

12. £10.23 or 1023 p

EXERCISE 1d
(p. 4)

1. 11	**2.** 12	**3.** 14	**4.** 5	**5.** 7

6. 12	**11.** 13	**16.** 4
7. 15	**12.** 3	**17.** 5
8. 9	**13.** 11	**18.** 6
9. 8	**14.** 8	**19.** 14
10. 6	**15.** 10	**20.** 8

EXERCISE 1e
(p. 5)

1. 211	**5.** 73	**9.** 126
2. 551	**6.** 141	**10.** 186
3. 406	**7.** 406	**11.** 470
4. 218	**8.** 126	**12.** 354

13. 287	**17.** 713	**21.** 8
14. 178	**18.** 255	**22.** 2828
15. 187	**19.** 279	**23.** 4823
16. 136	**20.** 149	**24.** 6615

25. 575	**29.** 703	**33.** 77
26. 3344	**30.** 676	**34.** 192
27. 1524	**31.** 4077	**35.** 4195
28. 189	**32.** 1048	**36.** 1644

EXERCISE 1f
(p. 6)

1. 403 p (or £4.03)	**3.** 85	**5.** 287	**7.** 213	**9.** 7500 m
2. 464	**4.** 89	**6.** 6483	**8.** 48	**10.** 19 cm

| **EXERCISE 1g** | **1.** 6 | **3.** 7 | **5.** 9 | **7.** 2 | **9.** 9 |
| **(p. 6)** | **2.** 5 | **4.** 4 | **6.** 4 | **8.** 7 | **10.** 7 |

EXERCISE 1h	**1.** 17	**6.** 28
(p. 7)	**2.** 5	**7.** 13
	3. 2	**8.** 3
	4. 20	**9.** 6
	5. 30	**10.** 4

11. 0	**16.** 50	**21.** 73	**26.** 597
12. 25	**17.** 0	**22.** 20	**27.** 19
13. 0	**18.** 39	**23.** 104	**28.** 129
14. 67	**19.** 0	**24.** 7	**29.** 250
15. 83	**20.** 95	**25.** 29	**30.** 65

EXERCISE 1i
(p. 8)
Intended for the above average but others may be able to obtain the answers with the help of a calculator.

| **1.** 10 p | **3.** 80 cm | **5.** 144 | **7.** 17 | **9.** 9 p |
| **2.** 72 | **4.** 318 | **6.** 69 lb | **8.** 45 |

| **EXERCISE 1j** | **1.** 8 | **3.** 5 | **5.** 1 | **7.** 23 | **9.** 7 |
| **(p. 9)** | **2.** 15 | **4.** 63 | **6.** 4 | **8.** 16 | **10.** 0 |

| **11.** 8 | **13.** 8 | **15.** 14 | **17.** 16 | **19.** 10 |
| **12.** 3 | **14** 12 | **16.** 5 | **18.** 38 | **20.** 20 |

21. 250, 257	**26.** 40, 38
22. 60, 56	**27.** 370, 366
23. 210, 209	**28.** 260, 264
24. 510, 507	**29.** 180, 176
25. 330, 334	**30.** 770, 777

31. 60, 58	**36.** 40, 42	**41.** 370, 360	**46.** 290, 293
32. 20, 16	**37.** 280, 284	**42.** 210, 206	**47.** 250, 250
33. 160, 163	**38.** 230, 229	**43.** 230, 227	**48.** 300, 291
34. 160, 154	**39.** 370, 362	**44.** 250, 251	**49.** 180, 170
35. 150, 148	**40.** 160, 160	**45.** 330, 328	**50.** 360, 353

CHAPTER 2 Multiplication and Division of Whole Numbers

The word "product" is used at the beginning of this chapter and will need explanation.

EXERCISE 2a
(p. 12)
Discussion of the properties of odd and even numbers is useful here, e.g. is the product of two even numbers even or odd and why? These properties can be used as simple checks on answers.

1. 46	**7.** 100	**13.** 126	**19.** 536
2. 126	**8.** 144	**14.** 588	**20.** 657
3. 104	**9.** 144	**15.** 324	**21.** 294
4. 304	**10.** 415	**16.** 292	**22.** 168
5. 290	**11.** 141	**17.** 162	**23.** 224
6. 93	**12.** 324	**18.** 132	**24.** 243

25. 608	**31.** 2859	**37.** 3174	**43.** 6784
26. 2456	**32.** 1632	**38.** 5142	**44.** 5931
27. 768	**33.** 2628	**39.** 3486	**45.** 5236
28. 388	**34.** 2184	**40.** 5211	**46.** 5552
29. 1989	**35.** 852	**41.** 4606	**47.** 1652
30. 844	**36.** 2565	**42.** 2989	**48.** 5157

EXERCISE 2b
(p. 13)

1. 270	**6.** 540	**11.** 29 200
2. 8200	**7.** 24 600	**12.** 3480
3. 360	**8.** 2040	**13.** 6630
4. 1080	**9.** 7800	**14.** 88 900
5. 256 000	**10.** 2800	**15.** 146 000

16. 35 100	**21.** 48 720	**26.** 42 800
17. 9420	**22.** 54 000	**27.** 19 200
18. 23 600	**23.** 38 920	**28.** 8800
19. 6160	**24.** 243 000	**29.** 19 000
20. 70 000	**25.** 35 100	**30.** 59 920

EXERCISE 2c
(p. 14)

1. 672	**6.** 1558	**11.** 7712
2. 559	**7.** 2782	**12.** 40 086
3. 1290	**8.** 4346	**13.** 398 793
4. 567	**9.** 7844	**14.** 35 028
5. 1428	**10.** 3204	**15.** 112 893

16. 107 520	**21.** 86 172	**26.** 36 575
17. 39 934	**22.** 56 648	**27.** 337 500
18. 70 952	**23.** 169 422	**28.** 453 750
19. 37 814	**24.** 191 430	**29.** 915 264
20. 565 915	**25.** 1 438 200	**30.** 1 203 000

EXERCISE 2d
(p. 15) Checks other than the estimate should be encouraged, e.g. is it even or odd, does it end in zero or five?

1. 2400	**6.** 1200	**11.** 18 000
2. 900	**7.** 1200	**12.** 24 000
3. 3200	**8.** 3600	**13.** 60 000
4. 1500	**9.** 3000	**14.** 300 000
5. 9000	**10.** 15 000	**15.** 240 000

16. 300 000, 244 326	**21.** 7200, 7098	**26.** 40 000, 42 692
17. 12 000, 11 136	**22.** 6000, 8750	**27.** 45 000, 42 987
18. 12 000, 10 192	**23.** 30 000, 32 406	**28.** 50 000, 46 657
19. 36 000, 34 225	**24.** 30 000, 30 012	**29.** 600 000, 579 424
20. 16 000, 18 768	**25.** 7200, 6612	**30.** 300 000, 298 717

31. 5600, 5382	**36.** 45 000, 40 281	**41.** 24 000, 23 458
32. 45 000, 40 091	**37.** 24 000, 22 222	**42.** 200 000, 231 548
33. 54 000, 51 888	**38.** 560 000, 563 997	**43.** 480 000, 465 234
34. 1000, 846	**39.** 25 000, 23 124	**44.** 4 900 000, 5 053 014
35. 6000, 6076	**40.** 35 000, 35 972	**45.** 350 000, 346 320

EXERCISE 2e If it has not been done earlier, this is an appropriate place to introduce the more able
(p. 16) pupils to a more formal setting down of answers.

1. 8188	**3.** 272	**5.** 22 500	**7.** 2592	**9.** 792
2. 10 896	**4.** 840	**6.** 1428	**8.** 420	**10.** 672

EXERCISE 2f Not intended for use with a calculator.
(p. 18)

1. 29	**6.** 48 r1	**11.** 9 r6
2. 14	**7.** 14 r3	**12.** 12 r1
3. 6	**8.** 20 r3	**13.** 13
4. 19	**9.** 23	**14.** 2 r3
5. 18	**10.** 13 r4	**15.** 13

16. 27	**21.** 171	**26.** 32 r6
17. 213	**22.** 231	**27.** 81 r3
18. 274	**23.** 103	**28.** 85
19. 201 r2	**24.** 71 r3	**29.** 121 r3
20. 124 r1	**25.** 24	**30.** 140 r2

31. 1167	**36.** 1067 r3	**41.** 198 r6
32. 440 r3	**37.** 1479 r4	**42.** 183
33. 2414 r1	**38.** 2193	**43.** 354 r3
34. 351 r3	**39.** 1214	**44.** 1727 r2
35. 428	**40.** 287	**45.** 1501

EXERCISE 2g Not intended for use with a calculator.
(p. 19)

1. 25 r6	**5.** 4 r910	**9.** 9 r426
2. 8 r7	**6.** 5 r7	**10.** 85 r12
3. 1 r96	**7.** 18 r6	**11.** 30 r77
4. 27 r83	**8.** 278 r1	**12.** 5 r704

EXERCISE 2h Not intended for use with a calculator.
(p. 19)

1. 12 r14	**5.** 20 r14	**9.** 16 r21
2. 52 r9	**6.** 8 r11	**10.** 21 r4
3. 18 r1	**7.** 35 r0	**11.** 28 r13
4. 34 r12	**8.** 16 r13	**12.** 22 r20

13. 215 r9	**17.** 127 r22	**21.** 221 r0
14. 348 r7	**18.** 86 r28	**22.** 135 r24
15. 246 r28	**19.** 75 r0	**23.** 236 r0
16. 456 r1	**20.** 120 r21	**24.** 217 r15

25. 304 r19	**29.** 202 r22	**33.** 83 r29
26. 573 r7	**30.** 89 r24	**34.** 146 r34
27. 96 r28	**31.** 200 r13	**35.** 77 r9
28. 64 r8	**32.** 65 r14	**36.** 469 r1

37. 2 r33	**41.** 25 r0	**45.** 11 r6
38. 107 r17	**42.** 111 r5	**46.** 20 r10
39. 111 r13	**43.** 90 r30	**47.** 20 r4
40. 190 r20	**44.** 200 r0	**48.** 42 r38

49. 7 r87	**53.** 12 r6	**57.** 6 r142
50. 26 r15	**54.** 56 r91	**58.** 74 r44
51. 24 r65	**55.** 25 r75	**59.** 27 r109
52. 32 r200	**56.** 20 r110	**60.** 22 r152

EXERCISE 2i
(p. 21)

Not intended for use with a calculator. If calculators are used to check answers, tuition on their use for mixed operations will be needed and will vary with the type of calculator used. A simple four-function calculator does not usually give priority to × and ÷ but a scientific calculator usually does and if pupils have a calculator with this facility it should be used.

1. 18	**6.** 5	**11.** 9	**16.** 10
2. 0	**7.** 22	**12.** 17	**17.** 3
3. 12	**8.** 7	**13.** 2	**18.** 13
4. 19	**9.** 7	**14.** 5	**19.** 26
5. 0	**10.** 21	**15.** 1	**20.** 6

21. 8	**26.** 8	**31.** 21	**36.** 9
22. 22	**27.** 10	**32.** 14	**37.** 16
23. 13	**28.** 8	**33.** 12	**38.** 14
24. 17	**29.** 5	**34.** 13	**39.** 14
25. 6	**30.** 9	**35.** 32	**40.** 30

EXERCISE 2j
(p. 22)

Not for use with a calculator.

1. 2	**6.** 8
2. 56	**7.** 49
3. 9	**8.** 2
4. 14	**9.** 45
5. 15	**10.** 2

11. 17	**16.** 7	**21.** 45	**26.** 1
12. 3	**17.** 30	**22.** 6	**27.** 4
13. 17	**18.** 1	**23.** 14	**28.** 25
14. 2	**19.** 4	**24.** 0	**29.** 1
15. 11	**20.** 36	**25.** 10	**30.** 18

EXERCISE 2k (p. 23)   Intended for the above average; with the others it should be approached with caution or omitted.

1. 6 and 2 p over
2. 68 p
3. 14
4. 18
5. 8 p
6. 15 p
7. 150 miles
8. 74
9. £1.45
10. 16 and 2 kg over
11. 76
12. 40 p
13. 20 p
14. 90
15. 840 cm
16. 9 p, 18 p, 33 p
17. 412 p (or £4.12)
18. £21
19. 225 275
20. 54 (one not full)
21. 67
22. 1831 or 1832 depending on her birth date
23. 26
24. 124
25. 600 m
26. 12 min
27. 15
28. 15 p
29. 34
30. 1 h; 25 min

EXERCISE 2l (p. 26)   Gives interesting variations on straightforward arithmetic.

1.

8	1	6
3	5	7
4	9	2

2.

4	9	2
3	5	7
8	1	6

3.

2	14	7	11
15	3	10	6
9	5	16	4
8	12	1	13

5. 9, 11
6. 13, 16
7. 4, 2
8. 17, 21
9. 32, 64
10. 15, 18
11. 4, 2
12. 81, 243
13. 36, 49
14. 10 000, 100 000
15. 45, 36
16. 19, 23
17. 37, 50

18.
$$1+3+5+7+9 \qquad = 25 = 5 \times 5$$
$$1+3+5+7+9+11 \qquad = 36 = 6 \times 6$$
$$1+3+5+7+9+11+13 = 49 = 7 \times 7$$

   a) 64   b) 400

19. $2+4+6+8+10$ $= 30 = 5 \times 6$
$2+4+6+8+10+12$ $= 42 = 6 \times 7$
$2+4+6+8+10+12+14 = 56 = 7 \times 8$

12

20. 1 5 10 10 5 1
1 6 15 20 15 6 1
1 7 21 35 35 21 7 1

21. 35

24. a) 1, 4, 9, 16   b) 25   c) 36, 49
d) 7, 9, these differences go up by 2 each time

25. a) 1, 3, 6, 10, 15, 21, 28
b) 2, 3, 4, 5, 6, 7
c) 1, 1, 1, 1, 1

26. 3, 8, 13, 18, . . . , 38, . . .

27. 1, 2, 4, 8, . . . , 32, . . .

28. a) (i) 20, 24, 28   (ii) 4   (iii) 0
b) (i) 24, 29, 34   (ii) 5   (iii) 0
c) (i) 32, 64, 128   (ii) 2, 4, 8, 16, 32, 64
(iii) 2, 4, 8, 16, 32
d) (i) 162, 486, 1458   (ii) 4, 12, 36, 108, 324, 972
(iii) 8, 24, 72, 216, 648
in (ii) and (iii), multiply by 3 each time

29. 1, 2, 3, 5, 8, 13, 21, 34, 55, 89, 144, . . .

30. 1, 2, 2, 4, 8, 32, 256, 8192, . . .

31. 15 and 33.   . . . add 6 each time

32. 1 and $\frac{1}{4}$.   . . . divide by 2 each time

33. 3 and 9.   . . . multiply by 3 each time

34. a) 9   b) 15

35. a) 15   b) 36

EXERCISE 2m **1.** 1005   **3.** 684   **5.** 6608   **7.** 242   **9.** 6 (10 p over)
(p. 30)   **2.** 17   **4.** 28   **6.** 1018   **8.** 7   **10.** 46 p

EXERCISE 2n **1.** 870   **3.** 672   **5.** 29   **7.** 50   **9.** 7 (3 left)
(p. 30)   **2.** 54   **4.** 9 r7   **6.** 118   **8.** 37   **10.** 5

EXERCISE 2p **1.** 2304   **3.** 413   **5.** 277 r8   **7.** 260   **9.** 35, 45
(p. 31)   **2.** 263   **4.** 3392   **6.** 393 r3   **8.** 19 r133   **10.** 33

EXERCISE 2q **1.** 3133   **3.** 8200   **5.** 278 r1   **7.** 3   **9.** 34 p
(p. 31)   **2.** 169   **4.** 4544   **6.** 713   **8.** 132

CHAPTER 3   Fractions: Addition and Subtraction

EXERCISE 3a
(p. 33)

1. $\frac{1}{6}$ 4. $\frac{5}{6}$ 7. $\frac{1}{4}$ 9. $\frac{1}{2}$

2. $\frac{3}{8}$ 5. $\frac{2}{6}$ 8. $\frac{3}{4}$ 10. $\frac{3}{10}$

3. $\frac{1}{3}$ 6. $\frac{7}{10}$

11. $\frac{5}{12}$ 14. $\frac{2}{6}$

12. $\frac{1}{4}$ 15. $\frac{4}{8}$

13. $\frac{3}{7}$ 16. $\frac{1}{6}$

EXERCISE 3b
(p. 34)

This may be used for discussion.

1. a) $\frac{1}{60}$ b) $\frac{9}{60}$ c) $\frac{30}{60}$ d) $\frac{45}{60}$ 11. $\frac{150}{500}$

2. $\frac{5}{7}$ 12. $\frac{45}{120}$

3. $\frac{11}{31}$ 13. $\frac{37}{3600}$

4. $\frac{51}{365}$ 14. $\frac{35}{80}$

5. $\frac{35}{100}$ 15. a) $\frac{10}{32}$ b) $\frac{8}{32}$ c) $\frac{25}{32}$

6. $\frac{90}{500}$ 16. $\frac{15}{40}, \frac{25}{40}$

7. $\frac{35}{180}$ 17. a) $\frac{20}{62}$ b) $\frac{10}{62}$ c) $\frac{48}{62}$

8. $\frac{3}{31}$ 18. a) $\frac{12}{37}$ b) $\frac{8}{37}$ c) $\frac{29}{37}$

9. $\frac{17}{61}$ 19. a) $\frac{9}{14}$ b) $\frac{3}{14}$

10. $\frac{5}{21}$

EXERCISE 3c
(p. 37)

7. 6   11. 18   15. 100

8. 4   12. 4   16. 6

9. 21   13. 15   17. 16

10. 36   14. 12   18. 18

19. 18   24. 8   29. 90

20. 30   25. 300   30. 8000

21. 10   26. 110   31. 55

22. 10   27. 40   32. 500

23. 100   28. 1000   33. 10 000

34. a) $\frac{12}{24}$ b) $\frac{8}{24}$ c) $\frac{4}{24}$ d) $\frac{18}{24}$ e) $\frac{10}{24}$ f) $\frac{9}{24}$

35. a) $\frac{6}{45}$ b) $\frac{20}{45}$ c) $\frac{27}{45}$ d) $\frac{15}{45}$ e) $\frac{42}{45}$ f) $\frac{9}{45}$

36. a) $\frac{27}{36}$ b) $\frac{20}{36}$ c) $\frac{6}{36}$ d) $\frac{10}{36}$ e) $\frac{21}{36}$ f) $\frac{24}{36}$

37. a) $\frac{12}{72}$ b) $\frac{12}{16}$ c) $\frac{12}{14}$ d) $\frac{12}{15}$ e) $\frac{12}{18}$ f) $\frac{12}{24}$

38. b) $\frac{2}{3} = \frac{6}{9}$ e) $\frac{7}{10} = \frac{70}{100}$

EXERCISE 3d
(p. 38)

1. $\frac{1}{2}$ 7. $\frac{3}{7}$ 13. $\frac{3}{11}$ 19. $\frac{3}{11}$

2. $\frac{5}{6}$ 8. $\frac{5}{6}$ 14. $\frac{5}{7}$ 20. $\frac{7}{9}$

3. $\frac{4}{5}$ 9. $\frac{3}{8}$ 15. $\frac{5}{11}$ 21. $\frac{9}{11}$

4. $\frac{2}{9}$ 10. $\frac{6}{7}$ 16. $\frac{4}{11}$ 22. $\frac{2}{5}$

5. $\frac{3}{8}$ 11. $\frac{3}{5}$ 17. $\frac{2}{7}$ 23. $\frac{3}{5}$

6. $\frac{3}{4}$ 12. $\frac{3}{4}$ 18. $\frac{5}{8}$ 24. $\frac{5}{8}$

25. $<$ **29.** $>$ **33.** $<$
26. $>$ **30.** $<$ **34.** $>$
27. $<$ **31.** $<$ **35.** $<$
28. $<$ **32.** $>$ **36.** $>$

37. $\frac{7}{30}, \frac{1}{2}, \frac{3}{5}, \frac{2}{3}$ **43.** $\frac{5}{6}, \frac{7}{9}, \frac{2}{3}, \frac{11}{18}, \frac{1}{2}$
38. $\frac{4}{10}, \frac{5}{8}, \frac{13}{20}, \frac{3}{4}$ **44.** $\frac{3}{4}, \frac{7}{10}, \frac{13}{20}, \frac{3}{5}, \frac{1}{2}$
39. $\frac{1}{3}, \frac{1}{2}, \frac{7}{12}, \frac{5}{6}$ **45.** $\frac{3}{4}, \frac{17}{24}, \frac{2}{3}, \frac{7}{12}, \frac{1}{6}$
40. $\frac{3}{8}, \frac{2}{5}, \frac{1}{2}, \frac{7}{10}, \frac{17}{20}$ **46.** $\frac{4}{5}, \frac{23}{30}, \frac{11}{15}, \frac{7}{10}, \frac{2}{3}$
41. $\frac{1}{2}, \frac{17}{28}, \frac{5}{7}, \frac{3}{4}, \frac{11}{14}$ **47.** $\frac{3}{4}, \frac{5}{8}, \frac{19}{32}, \frac{1}{2}, \frac{7}{16}$
42. $\frac{2}{5}, \frac{1}{2}, \frac{14}{25}, \frac{3}{5}, \frac{7}{10}$ **48.** $\frac{5}{6}, \frac{4}{5}, \frac{3}{4}, \frac{7}{12}, \frac{1}{2}$

Simplifying fractions: this is the first time that the word "factor" is used. It will need explanation and much discussion to clarify its meaning, e.g. is 2 a factor of 14; what are the factors of 6? Factors are discussed again in Chapter 12, and Exercise 12a could be done now.

Children not familiar with simplifying fractions need a lot of discussion before they do any themselves. Discussion of the other words used for simplifying is needed, i.e. reducing and cancelling. (Cancelling really means the act of removing the common factors.)

EXERCISE 3e
(p. 42)

1. $\frac{1}{3}$ **3.** $\frac{1}{3}$ **5.** $\frac{1}{3}$ **7.** $\frac{1}{3}$ **9.** $\frac{1}{2}$
2. $\frac{3}{5}$ **4.** $\frac{1}{2}$ **6.** $\frac{1}{2}$ **8.** $\frac{2}{3}$ **10.** $\frac{1}{4}$

11. $\frac{2}{7}$ **13.** $\frac{1}{5}$ **15.** $\frac{2}{7}$ **17.** $\frac{1}{2}$ **19.** $\frac{3}{5}$
12. $\frac{3}{10}$ **14.** $\frac{2}{5}$ **16.** $\frac{1}{3}$ **18.** $\frac{1}{5}$ **20.** $\frac{2}{5}$

21. $\frac{5}{9}$ **23.** $\frac{3}{4}$ **25.** $\frac{4}{5}$ **27.** $\frac{1}{3}$ **29.** $\frac{3}{4}$
22. $\frac{7}{11}$ **24.** $\frac{3}{11}$ **26.** $\frac{4}{7}$ **28.** $\frac{9}{11}$ **30.** $\frac{4}{5}$

EXERCISE 3f
(p. 43)

1. $\frac{3}{4}$ **5.** $\frac{19}{23}$ **9.** $\frac{11}{21}$
2. $\frac{1}{2}$ **6.** $\frac{3}{7}$ **10.** $\frac{1}{2}$
3. $\frac{5}{11}$ **7.** $\frac{3}{5}$ **11.** $\frac{11}{13}$
4. $\frac{10}{13}$ **8.** $\frac{2}{5}$ **12.** $\frac{4}{5}$

13. $\frac{6}{7}$ **17.** $\frac{3}{4}$ **21.** $\frac{6}{11}$
14. $\frac{9}{17}$ **18.** $\frac{11}{19}$ **22.** $\frac{15}{23}$
15. $\frac{1}{2}$ **19.** $\frac{1}{2}$ **23.** $\frac{8}{9}$
16. $\frac{9}{10}$ **20.** $\frac{2}{5}$ **24.** $\frac{2}{3}$

25. $\frac{4}{5}$ **28.** $\frac{11}{14}$ **31.** $\frac{13}{30}$ **33.** $\frac{1}{2}$
26. $\frac{2}{5}$ **29.** $\frac{9}{17}$ **32.** $\frac{5}{9}$ **34.** $\frac{25}{99}$
27. $\frac{23}{31}$ **30.** $\frac{12}{19}$

Addition and subtraction of fractions: many pupils try to add or subtract at the same time as changing denominators and are then baffled by their inevitable mistakes. This is a case where they should be encouraged to write down each step, as shown in the worked examples, so that they separate the two operations.

EXERCISE 3g
(p. 45)

1. $\frac{13}{15}$
2. $\frac{23}{40}$
3. $\frac{11}{30}$
4. $\frac{29}{35}$

5. $\frac{29}{30}$
6. $\frac{39}{56}$
7. $\frac{25}{42}$
8. $\frac{20}{21}$

9. $\frac{19}{42}$
10. $\frac{41}{42}$
11. $\frac{82}{99}$
12. $\frac{47}{90}$

13. $\frac{7}{10}$
14. $\frac{13}{16}$
15. $\frac{17}{21}$
16. $\frac{33}{100}$

17. $\frac{19}{20}$
18. $\frac{5}{8}$
19. $\frac{8}{9}$
20. $\frac{13}{18}$

21. $\frac{13}{20}$
22. $\frac{13}{22}$
23. $\frac{13}{15}$
24. $\frac{3}{4}$

25. $\frac{19}{20}$
26. $\frac{17}{24}$
27. $\frac{19}{20}$
28. $\frac{11}{12}$

29. $\frac{6}{7}$
30. 1
31. $\frac{39}{40}$
32. $\frac{13}{18}$

33. $\frac{17}{20}$
34. $\frac{17}{18}$
35. $\frac{19}{30}$
36. $\frac{2}{3}$

EXERCISE 3h
(p. 47)

1. $\frac{2}{3}$
2. $\frac{1}{2}$
3. $\frac{5}{17}$
4. $\frac{11}{20}$

5. $\frac{2}{5}$
6. $\frac{3}{7}$
7. $\frac{5}{13}$
8. $\frac{3}{5}$

9. $\frac{5}{21}$
10. $\frac{5}{21}$
11. $\frac{7}{15}$
12. $\frac{1}{3}$

13. $\frac{18}{55}$
14. $\frac{1}{9}$
15. $\frac{3}{26}$
16. $\frac{1}{12}$

17. $\frac{9}{100}$
18. $\frac{19}{56}$
19. $\frac{3}{16}$
20. $\frac{4}{15}$

21. $\frac{1}{8}$
22. $\frac{1}{4}$
23. $\frac{1}{6}$
24. $\frac{4}{15}$

EXERCISE 3i
(p. 49)

1. $\frac{3}{8}$
2. $\frac{5}{7}$
3. $\frac{1}{16}$
4. $\frac{5}{12}$

5. $\frac{9}{50}$
6. $\frac{5}{12}$
7. $\frac{3}{5}$
8. $\frac{17}{18}$

9. $\frac{17}{50}$
10. $\frac{1}{2}$
11. $\frac{3}{4}$
12. $\frac{1}{2}$

13. $\frac{1}{18}$
14. $\frac{1}{12}$
15. $\frac{1}{5}$
16. $\frac{1}{16}$

17. $\frac{2}{9}$
18. $\frac{7}{20}$
19. $\frac{1}{8}$
20. $\frac{1}{3}$

21. $\frac{19}{100}$
22. $\frac{1}{4}$
23. $\frac{5}{18}$
24. $\frac{1}{30}$

EXERCISE 3j   Intended for the above average; can be used for discussion with others.
(p. 50)

1. $\frac{13}{15}, \frac{2}{15}$ **3.** $\frac{1}{3}, \frac{1}{12}$ **5.** $\frac{11}{40}, \frac{19}{20}, \frac{7}{40}$

2. $\frac{11}{15}, \frac{4}{15}$ **4.** $\frac{3}{8}, \frac{7}{8}$

EXERCISE 3k   **1.** $2\frac{1}{4}$ **3.** $6\frac{1}{6}$ **5.** $9\frac{7}{9}$ **7.** $6\frac{3}{4}$ **9.** $25\frac{2}{5}$
(p. 52)   **2.** $4\frac{3}{4}$ **4.** $5\frac{3}{10}$ **6.** $3\frac{1}{2}$ **8.** $5\frac{1}{8}$ **10.** $10\frac{4}{11}$

11. $13\frac{5}{8}$ **13.** $13\frac{4}{9}$ **15.** $7\frac{10}{11}$ **17.** $13\frac{2}{3}$ **19.** $24\frac{1}{3}$
12. $11\frac{6}{7}$ **14.** $15\frac{1}{6}$ **16.** $12\frac{5}{6}$ **18.** $13\frac{2}{5}$ **20.** $4\frac{9}{10}$

EXERCISE 3l   **1.** $\frac{13}{3}$ **3.** $\frac{17}{10}$ **5.** $\frac{57}{7}$ **7.** $\frac{20}{7}$ **9.** $\frac{11}{3}$
(p. 52)   **2.** $\frac{33}{4}$ **4.** $\frac{98}{9}$ **6.** $\frac{33}{5}$ **8.** $\frac{25}{6}$ **10.** $\frac{11}{2}$

11. $\frac{37}{5}$ **13.** $\frac{19}{5}$ **15.** $\frac{35}{4}$ **17.** $\frac{19}{10}$ **19.** $\frac{59}{8}$
12. $\frac{22}{9}$ **14.** $\frac{43}{9}$ **16.** $\frac{73}{7}$ **18.** $\frac{20}{3}$ **20.** $\frac{101}{10}$

EXERCISE 3m   **1.** $5\frac{1}{7}$ **5.** $16\frac{2}{5}$ **9.** $8\frac{1}{6}$
(p. 53)   **2.** $9\frac{5}{6}$ **6.** $7\frac{1}{4}$ **10.** $10\frac{7}{10}$
3. $4\frac{8}{11}$ **7.** $13\frac{2}{3}$ **11.** $7\frac{2}{5}$
4. $2\frac{1}{2}$ **8.** $7\frac{1}{9}$ **12.** $6\frac{1}{2}$

EXERCISE 3n   Again it is important to encourage the writing down of each step so that only
(p. 54)   one operation is performed at a time.

1. $5\frac{3}{4}$ **6.** $4\frac{1}{6}$
2. $3\frac{5}{6}$ **7.** $4\frac{9}{20}$
3. $5\frac{23}{40}$ **8.** $3\frac{3}{14}$
4. $9\frac{4}{9}$ **9.** $7\frac{7}{10}$
5. $5\frac{29}{36}$ **10.** $13\frac{17}{21}$

11. $10\frac{13}{16}$ **16.** $11\frac{9}{10}$ **21.** $11\frac{1}{2}$ **26.** $15\frac{4}{5}$
12. $6\frac{1}{3}$ **17.** $8\frac{3}{10}$ **22.** $17\frac{3}{7}$ **27.** $14\frac{51}{100}$
13. $11\frac{3}{14}$ **18.** $18\frac{1}{2}$ **23.** $17\frac{3}{16}$ **28.** $17\frac{13}{32}$
14. $8\frac{1}{16}$ **19.** $10\frac{1}{10}$ **24.** $21\frac{1}{18}$ **29.** $22\frac{2}{7}$
15. $12\frac{1}{16}$ **20.** $11\frac{1}{10}$ **25.** $15\frac{2}{5}$ **30.** $22\frac{1}{2}$

EXERCISE 3p   **1.** $1\frac{5}{8}$ **5.** $5\frac{5}{12}$ **9.** $1\frac{7}{10}$
(p. 56)   **2.** $1\frac{13}{15}$ **6.** $1\frac{1}{2}$ **10.** $3\frac{11}{35}$
3. $1\frac{1}{6}$ **7.** $1\frac{5}{14}$ **11.** $2\frac{2}{15}$
4. $\frac{3}{4}$ **8.** $2\frac{3}{10}$ **12.** $3\frac{1}{4}$

13. $3\frac{3}{10}$ **17.** $1\frac{3}{4}$ **21.** $3\frac{3}{28}$

14. $2\frac{4}{63}$ **18.** $3\frac{7}{20}$ **22.** $1\frac{5}{8}$

15. $3\frac{7}{24}$ **19.** $3\frac{9}{35}$ **23.** $\frac{3}{4}$

16. $2\frac{25}{28}$ **20.** $6\frac{2}{33}$ **24.** $1\frac{27}{35}$

25. $1\frac{3}{8}$ **29.** $\frac{7}{9}$ **33.** $3\frac{9}{10}$

26. $2\frac{7}{10}$ **30.** $1\frac{1}{2}$ **34.** $\frac{2}{3}$

27. $3\frac{1}{2}$ **31.** $2\frac{5}{6}$ **35.** $1\frac{1}{6}$

28. $2\frac{1}{2}$ **32.** $2\frac{7}{8}$ **36.** $2\frac{16}{21}$

EXERCISE 3q
(p. 56)

1. a) $1\frac{5}{21}$ b) $\frac{11}{24}$ c) $\frac{35}{72}$ d) $2\frac{1}{6}$ e) $\frac{11}{12}$

2. a) $2\frac{1}{4}$ b) $3\frac{1}{5}$

3. a) $\frac{3}{7}$ b) $\frac{17}{30}$

4. a) $\frac{1}{2}, \frac{3}{5}, \frac{13}{20}, \frac{7}{10}$ b) $\frac{7}{12}, \frac{2}{3}, \frac{3}{4}, \frac{5}{6}$ c) $\frac{3}{5}, \frac{7}{10}, \frac{71}{100}, \frac{17}{20}$

5. a) $<$ b) $>$ c) $>$

6. a) $\frac{3}{11}$ b) $\frac{7}{22}$ c) $\frac{9}{11}$

EXERCISE 3r
(p. 57)

1. a) $\frac{2}{15}$ b) $1\frac{7}{10}$ c) $\frac{3}{22}$ d) $6\frac{7}{12}$ e) $\frac{1}{2}$ f) $2\frac{13}{20}$

2. a) $\frac{7}{8}$ b) $1\frac{5}{6}$ c) $\frac{12}{13}$

3. a) $\frac{13}{100}$ b) $\frac{233}{366}$

4. a) $>$ b) $<$ c) $<$

5. a) $\frac{3}{10}, \frac{7}{20}, \frac{3}{8}, \frac{2}{5}$ b) $\frac{3}{10}, \frac{2}{5}, \frac{7}{15}, \frac{1}{2}$ c) $\frac{17}{32}, \frac{9}{16}, \frac{5}{8}, \frac{3}{4}$

6. a) $\frac{15}{28}$ b) $\frac{2}{7}$

EXERCISE 3s
(p. 57)

1. a) $\frac{43}{140}$ b) $\frac{17}{45}$ c) $\frac{1}{8}$ d) $3\frac{1}{12}$ e) 0 f) 5

2. a) $1\frac{3}{8}$ b) $2\frac{2}{5}$ c) $\frac{5}{16}$

3. a) $<$ b) $<$

4. a) $\frac{1}{2}, \frac{3}{5}, \frac{3}{4}, \frac{5}{6}$ b) $\frac{1}{2}, \frac{5}{9}, \frac{2}{3}, \frac{5}{6}$

5. a) $\frac{7}{60}$ b) $\frac{1}{3}$ c) $\frac{38}{79}$

6. a) $\frac{17}{19}$ b) $\frac{13}{19}$

EXERCISE 3t
(p. 58)

1. a) $1\frac{1}{6}$ b) $\frac{5}{8}$ c) $\frac{1}{12}$ d) $2\frac{9}{20}$ e) $\frac{11}{12}$ f) $3\frac{2}{3}$

2. a) $4\frac{3}{8}$ b) $\frac{1}{8}$ c) $2\frac{4}{7}$

3. a) $\frac{5}{24}$ b) $\frac{1}{10}$ c) $\frac{5}{12}$

4. a) $>$ b) $<$

5. a) $\frac{5}{11}, \frac{1}{2}, \frac{23}{44}, \frac{13}{22}$ b) $\frac{5}{9}, \frac{7}{12}, \frac{2}{3}, \frac{3}{4}$

6. a) $\frac{1}{5}$ b) $\frac{8}{15}$ c) $\frac{1}{3}$

CHAPTER 4   Fractions: Multiplication and Division

If pupils have not done multiplication of fractions before, much classroom discussion is advisable, using cake diagrams, rectangles, etc., to get across the meaning that, for example, $\frac{1}{2} \times \frac{3}{4}$ means $\frac{1}{2}$ of $\frac{3}{4}$ and that $\frac{1}{2} \times \frac{3}{4} = \frac{1 \times 3}{2 \times 4}$.

EXERCISE 4b
(p. 60)

1. $\frac{3}{8}$
2. $\frac{10}{21}$
3. $\frac{2}{15}$
4. $\frac{7}{16}$

5. $\frac{3}{7}$
6. $\frac{4}{63}$
7. $\frac{6}{35}$
8. $\frac{6}{25}$

9. $\frac{5}{24}$
10. $\frac{14}{27}$
11. $\frac{3}{20}$
12. $\frac{3}{35}$

13. $\frac{1}{6}$
14. $\frac{4}{7}$

15. $\frac{7}{18}$
16. $\frac{2}{3}$

17. $\frac{1}{9}$
18. $\frac{15}{28}$

19. $\frac{3}{4}$
20. $\frac{6}{7}$

21. $\frac{5}{48}$
22. $\frac{11}{20}$

23. $\frac{4}{11}$
24. $\frac{4}{11}$

25. $\frac{2}{9}$
26. $\frac{2}{31}$
27. $\frac{2}{3}$
28. $\frac{1}{5}$

29. $\frac{1}{7}$
30. $\frac{3}{16}$
31. $\frac{3}{20}$
32. $\frac{2}{3}$

33. 4
34. $\frac{1}{18}$
35. $\frac{3}{22}$
36. $\frac{1}{6}$

EXERCISE 4c
(p. 61)

1. $\frac{3}{5}$
2. 2
3. $\frac{3}{4}$
4. $11\frac{1}{5}$
5. $\frac{1}{2}$

6. $\frac{1}{2}$
7. $\frac{7}{8}$
8. 2
9. $16\frac{1}{3}$
10. $\frac{17}{21}$

11. 14
12. 4
13. 30
14. $16\frac{1}{2}$
15. $7\frac{1}{2}$

16. 9
17. 10
18. 10
19. 20
20. 60

21. 7
22. 15
23. 5
24. $6\frac{1}{3}$
25. 23

26. 9
27. 14
28. 12
29. 3
30. 8

EXERCISE 4d
(p. 63)

1. 23
2. 30
3. $12\frac{1}{2}$
4. $37\frac{1}{2}$

5. 110
6. $13\frac{1}{2}$
7. 36
8. $8\frac{1}{2}$

9. 120
10. $18\frac{1}{3}$
11. 14
12. 44

EXERCISE 4e
(p. 63)

1. 6
2. 6
3. 3
4. 16
5. 10

6. 6
7. 5
8. 8
9. 30
10. 15

11. 12 m
12. 25 dollars
13. 45 litres
14. 33 miles
15. 21 gallons

16. 8 m
17. 10 dollars
18. 28 litres
19. 15 miles
20. 88 gallons

21. 50 p
22. 8 p
23. 30 p
24. 12 p
25. 292 days

26. 9 h
27. 1 day
28. £3
29. 60 p
30. 21 h

Division: if not already done, much discussion is necessary before deducing the "rule".

EXERCISE 4f **1.** 14   **2.** 20   **3.** 21   **4.** 15   **5.** 12
(p. 64)

6. 10   **10.** 30   **14.** 99
7. 21   **11.** 18   **15.** 39
8. 45   **12.** 16   **16.** 63
9. 99   **13.** 49   **17.** 38

18. $\frac{3}{4}$ **20.** $\frac{1}{12}$ **22.** $\frac{2}{5}$
19. $1\frac{1}{5}$ **21.** $1\frac{1}{2}$ **23.** 1

24. $2\frac{1}{3}$ **26.** $1\frac{1}{2}$ **28.** $\frac{2}{3}$
25. $\frac{2}{3}$ **27.** $1\frac{2}{5}$ **29.** $\frac{3}{8}$

EXERCISE 4g **1.** $10\frac{1}{2}$ **6.** $6\frac{2}{3}$ **11.** 6   **16.** 6
(p. 66)   **2.** $\frac{5}{6}$ **7.** $\frac{9}{10}$ **12.** $2\frac{2}{3}$ **17.** $1\frac{3}{7}$
3. $5\frac{1}{3}$ **8.** $4\frac{5}{6}$ **13.** 12   **18.** $3\frac{1}{3}$
4. 6   **9.** $1\frac{4}{5}$ **14.** 6   **19.** $1\frac{1}{2}$
5. $2\frac{8}{11}$ **10.** 4   **15.** $5\frac{3}{5}$ **20.** 12

EXERCISE 4h **1.** 1   **5.** $\frac{8}{15}$ **9.** $1\frac{1}{2}$
(p. 68)   **2.** $2\frac{1}{2}$ **6.** $2\frac{2}{3}$ **10.** $\frac{9}{32}$
3. $1\frac{2}{3}$ **7.** $5\frac{1}{10}$ **11.** $\frac{9}{20}$
4. $\frac{2}{3}$ **8.** $2\frac{1}{4}$ **12.** $\frac{4}{5}$

EXERCISE 4i Intended as extra practice for the above average.
(p. 69)
1. $\frac{3}{5}$ **6.** $\frac{5}{24}$ **11.** $\frac{2}{21}$ **16.** $\frac{9}{22}$
2. $\frac{7}{12}$ **7.** $1\frac{5}{8}$ **12.** $\frac{7}{10}$ **17.** $\frac{5}{21}$
3. $\frac{1}{5}$ **8.** $\frac{41}{42}$ **13.** $\frac{21}{34}$ **18.** $\frac{5}{18}$
4. $\frac{3}{14}$ **9.** $\frac{1}{16}$ **14.** $1\frac{1}{2}$ **19.** $\frac{2}{33}$
5. $\frac{13}{15}$ **10.** $\frac{1}{3}$ **15.** $\frac{1}{22}$ **20.** $1\frac{2}{25}$

21. $\frac{1}{21}$ **26.** $4\frac{2}{9}$ **31.** T   **36.** F
22. $1\frac{1}{4}$ **27.** $1\frac{3}{8}$ **32.** F   **37.** T
23. $\frac{1}{4}$ **28.** $2\frac{7}{30}$ **33.** T   **38.** F
24. $\frac{1}{3}$ **29.** $\frac{11}{16}$ **34.** T   **39.** F
25. $\frac{1}{9}$ **30.** $1\frac{8}{9}$ **35.** F   **40.** T

EXERCISE 4j **1.** $4\frac{3}{4}$ **6.** $\frac{17}{18}$ **11.** $6\frac{1}{4}$ **16.** $\frac{17}{20}$
(p. 70)   **2.** $1\frac{1}{8}$ **7.** 22   **12.** 2   **17.** $4\frac{1}{14}$
3. $\frac{3}{4}$ **8.** $\frac{13}{15}$ **13.** $1\frac{7}{10}$ **18.** $\frac{7}{8}$
4. 4   **9.** 3   **14.** $2\frac{2}{7}$ **19.** $3\frac{13}{16}$
5. $2\frac{1}{14}$ **10.** $3\frac{7}{8}$ **15.** $2\frac{2}{5}$ **20.** $4\frac{1}{2}$

21. $1\frac{1}{12}$ **26.** $1\frac{3}{8}$ **31.** $3\frac{1}{2}$ **36.** $\frac{3}{8}$

22. $\frac{7}{12}$ **27.** $3\frac{1}{20}$ **32.** 1   **37.** $\frac{1}{16}$

23. $5\frac{3}{8}$ **28.** $1\frac{1}{2}$ **33.** $2\frac{1}{4}$ **38.** $4\frac{2}{7}$

24. $3\frac{1}{12}$ **29.** $5\frac{3}{7}$ **34.** 0   **39.** $2\frac{6}{7}$

25. $\frac{7}{8}$ **30.** $\frac{1}{2}$ **35.** $\frac{1}{5}$ **40.** 2

EXERCISE 4k **1.** 30 kg   **3.** 3 km   **5.** 22
(p. 71)   **2.** $\frac{7}{20}$ litres   **4.** $58\frac{1}{2}$ min   **6.** $1\frac{1}{2}$

EXERCISE 4l **1.** a) $1\frac{2}{3}$ b) $2\frac{3}{8}$ **6.** a) $19\frac{1}{3}$ b) $1\frac{1}{2}$ **11.** a) 27 b) 40
(p. 72)   **2.** 6   **7.** $2\frac{1}{6}$ **12.** a) $2\frac{3}{5}$ b) $3\frac{7}{8}$ c) $5\frac{2}{5}$
                 3. $\frac{5}{6}$ **8.** 6   **13.** a) T b) T c) F
                 4. $1\frac{13}{20}$ **9.** 18 min   **14.** 63 min
                 5. $\frac{3}{5}, \frac{2}{3}, \frac{7}{10}$ **10.** $3\frac{9}{10}$ **15.** $124\frac{1}{2}$ g

EXERCISE 4m **1.** a) 15 b) $11\frac{1}{3}$ **5.** $\frac{1}{3}, \frac{2}{5}, \frac{7}{15}$ **9.** a) 24 b) 21
(p. 73)   **2.** $1\frac{2}{3}$ b) $4\frac{11}{18}$ **6.** 2   **10.** a) $3\frac{1}{8}$ b) $5\frac{4}{9}$ c) $6\frac{1}{6}$
                 3. a) < b) <   **7.** a) $6\frac{1}{4}$ b) $2\frac{6}{11}$ **11.** $12\frac{1}{8}$ km; $\frac{77}{97}$
                 4. a) $1\frac{1}{12}$ b) 9   **8.** 125 s   **12.** 6

EXERCISE 4n **1.** a) $2\frac{25}{36}$ b) 0   **5.** a) $6\frac{1}{4}$ b) $17\frac{11}{12}$ **9.** a) $7\frac{1}{3}$ b) $9\frac{1}{5}$ c) $10\frac{3}{5}$
(p. 74)   **2.** a) $\frac{1}{4}$ b) $\frac{4}{5}$ **6.** $\frac{8}{11}$ **10.** a, b and c
                 3. 25 days   **7.** $1\frac{6}{7}$ **11.** 18 min
                 4. $\frac{17}{20}, \frac{3}{4}, \frac{7}{10}$ **8.** $2\frac{2}{5}$ **12.** $1\frac{4}{7}$ kg

CHAPTER 5   Introduction to Decimals

EXERCISE 5b **1.** $\frac{1}{5}$ **5.** $\frac{1}{1000}$ **9.** $1\frac{4}{5}$
(p. 77)   **2.** $\frac{3}{50}$ **6.** $6\frac{2}{5}$ **10.** $1\frac{7}{10}$
                 3. $1\frac{3}{10}$ **7.** $\frac{7}{10}$ **11.** $15\frac{1}{2}$
                 4. $\frac{7}{10000}$ **8.** $2\frac{1}{100}$ **12.** $8\frac{3}{50}$

13. $\frac{73}{100}$ **17.** $\frac{67}{100000}$ **21.** $\frac{207}{10000}$

14. $\frac{81}{1000}$ **18.** $\frac{17}{100}$ **22.** $\frac{63}{100}$

15. $\frac{207}{1000}$ **19.** $\frac{71}{1000}$ **23.** $\frac{31}{1000}$

16. $\frac{29}{10000}$ **20.** $\frac{3001}{10000}$ **24.** $\frac{47}{100}$

25. $\frac{1}{4}$ **29.** $\frac{3}{20}$ **33.** $\frac{11}{250}$

26. $\frac{9}{125}$ **30.** $\frac{1}{40}$ **34.** $\frac{1}{8}$

27. $\frac{19}{50}$ **31.** $\frac{7}{20}$ **35.** $\frac{12}{25}$

28. $\frac{61}{2000}$ **32.** $\frac{1}{625}$ **36.** $\frac{5}{8}$

EXERCISE 5c
(p. 79)

1. 0.03
2. 0.9
3. 1.1
4. 0.002

5. 0.4
6. 2.06
7. 0.04
8. 7.8

9. 7.08
10. 0.0006
11. 4.005
12. 0.0029

EXERCISE 5d
(p. 80)

1. 10.8
2. 7.55
3. 0.039
4. 3.98
5. 5.83

6. 14.04
7. 7.6
8. 12.24
9. 3.68
10. 9.12

11. 0.2673
12. 2.102
13. 0.001 76
14. 0.131
15. 4.698

16. 0.3552
17. 4.6005
18. 20.7
19. 6.798
20. 27.374

21. 2.38   22. 17.301   23. 15.62   24. 13.52   25. 16.81

EXERCISE 5e
(p. 81)

1. 2.5
2. 7.8
3. 18.5
4. 0.41

5. 0.0321
6. 16.87
7. 2.241
8. 0.191

9. 71.4
10. 6.65
11. 41.45
12. 6.939

13. 3.06
14. 2.94
15. 3.13
16. 2.66
17. 2.4

18. 7.882
19. 6.118
20. 2.772
21. 11.1974
22. 0.000 197

23. 0.0067
24. 0.0013
25. 0.005 27
26. 0.059 27
27. 5.27

28. 5.927
29. 7.24
30. 729.4
31. 0.729 94
32. 0.13

33. 57.6   34. 8.3   35. 0.149   36. 6.81

EXERCISE 5f
(p. 82)

1. 10.32
2. 6.92
3. 2.98
4. 6.6
5. 4.4

6. 100.28
7. 99.72
8. 0.286
9. 0.234
10. 77.62

11. 39.88
12. 36.52
13. 202.84
14. 17.76
15. 0.59

16. 0.007
17. 0.382
18. 6.64
19. 38.82
20. 7.81

21. 22.6 cm
22. 5.3 m

23. £24.77
24. £10.52

25. 1
26. 53.2 cm

27. £2.85
28. 5.9 cm

EXERCISE 5g
(p. 85)

1. 72 000
2. 82.4
3. 0.24
4. 460

5. 3278
6. 430
7. 6.02
8. 32.06

9. 72 810
10. 0.000 063
11. 0.703
12. 374

EXERCISE 5h
(p. 85)

1. 2.772
2. 7.626
3. 0.000 024
4. 0.014

5. 2.7
6. 0.068
7. 0.026
8. 0.0158

9. 0.0426
10. 1.34
11. 0.003 74
12. 0.0092

EXERCISE 5i
(p. 86)

1. 0.16	**5.** 1420	**9.** 0.14
2. 16	**6.** 6.8	**10.** 78 000
3. 7.8	**7.** 0.0163	**11.** 0.24
4. 0.000 78	**8.** 0.002	**12.** 63

13. 3.2	**17.** 11 100	**21.** 0.000 24
14. 0.079	**18.** 0.000 38	**22.** 0.000 003
15. 0.078	**19.** 0.000 38	**23.** 4.1
16. 0.24	**20.** 380 000	**24.** 10.04

25. 4.2 m	**27.** 0.138, 1380	**29.** 0.1746
26. £152	**28.** 0.16	**30.** 0.0038

EXERCISE 5j Designed for use without a calculator but some may benefit by using it.
(p. 86)

1. 0.2	**5.** 0.1	**9.** 21.3
2. 1.6	**6.** 0.19	**10.** 2.51
3. 0.21	**7.** 0.224	**11.** 1.64
4. 2.6	**8.** 3.8	**12.** 0.15

13. 0.019	**17.** 0.002	**21.** 0.308
14. 0.000 13	**18.** 0.000 06	**22.** 0.1092
15. 0.002 18	**19.** 0.81	**23.** 0.0057
16. 0.042	**20.** 1.06	**24.** 0.0453

25. 0.0019	**29.** 0.9	**33.** 2.107
26. 0.09	**30.** 0.0106	**34.** 0.62
27. 0.1043	**31.** 0.019	**35.** 0.037
28. 0.000 015	**32.** 0.77	**36.** 0.78

37. 1.2	**41.** 0.72	**45.** 4.55
38. 1.85	**42.** 0.000 04	**46.** 0.000 155
39. 0.415	**43.** 0.8875	**47.** 2.35
40. 0.15	**44.** 1.75	**48.** 0.0124

49. 0.125	**53.** 2.6	**57.** 0.853 75
50. 0.038 75	**54.** 0.05	**58.** 2.45
51. 0.52	**55.** 0.0025	**59.** 0.575
52. 1.905	**56.** 0.6028	**60.** 0.055 75

61. 3.65 cm	**63.** 7.15 kg	**65.** £4.50
62. 4.075 m	**64.** 3.2 cm	

EXERCISE 5k
(p. 89)

1. 1.1	**5.** 0.51	**9.** 0.53
2. 0.15	**6.** 3.2	**10.** 0.26
3. 0.12	**7.** 0.0041	**11.** 0.56
4. 0.45	**8.** 0.036	**12.** 0.7

13. 0.32   **17.** 3.2   **21.** 0.52
14. 0.26   **18.** 0.43   **22.** 3.12
15. 0.024   **19.** 0.21   **23.** 0.84
16. 0.000 23   **20.** 0.000 713   **24.** 0.005 68

EXERCISE 5l
(p. 89)

1. 0.25   **3.** 0.6   **5.** 0.04   **7.** 0.625   **9.** 0.12
2. 0.375   **4.** 0.3125   **6.** 2.8   **8.** 0.4375   **10.** 0.031 25

EXERCISE 5m
(p. 90)

1. $\frac{1}{5}$ **3.** $\frac{4}{5}$ **5.** $\frac{3}{5}$ **7.** $\frac{9}{10}$
2. $\frac{3}{10}$ **4.** $\frac{3}{4}$ **6.** $\frac{7}{10}$ **8.** $\frac{1}{20}$

9. 0.9   **11.** 0.8   **13.** 0.03   **15.** 0.625
10. 0.25   **12.** 0.375   **14.** 0.75   **16.** 0.07

EXERCISE 5n
(p. 90)

1. $\frac{1}{50}$ **3.** 36.87   **5.** 0.0205   **7.** 0.875
2. 0.009, 0.091   **4.** 2.38   **6.** 3.01   **8.** 20.72 cm

EXERCISE 5p
(p. 91)

1. $\frac{3}{10}$ **3.** 27.32   **5.** 0.06   **7.** 1.5
2. 0.14   **4.** 0.000 62   **6.** £10.58   **8.** $\frac{2}{5}$

EXERCISE 5q
(p. 91)

1. $\frac{1}{125}$ **3.** 27.79   **5.** 0.0086   **7.** 0.1875
2. 0.8   **4.** 85.04   **6.** 0.25   **8.** 4.8 cm

EXERCISE 5r
(p. 92)

1. 0.125   **3.** 0.26   **5.** $\frac{9}{100}$ **7.** 2.8
2. 6.28   **4.** 2.98   **6.** 280   **8.** £2.19

CHAPTER 6   Multiplication and Division of Decimals

EXERCISE 6a
(p. 93)   Can be used for discussion.

1. 0.008   **5.** 0.0003   **9.** 0.0008
2. 0.01   **6.** 0.000 04   **10.** 0.000 000 6
3. 0.018   **7.** 0.24   **11.** 0.018
4. 0.06   **8.** 0.000 48   **12.** 0.008

EXERCISE 6b
(p. 94)   Not intended for use with a calculator but discretion is needed in Nos. 19–40.

1. 0.18   **5.** 0.0108   **9.** 0.0064
2. 0.0024   **6.** 0.000 021   **10.** 0.0018
3. 0.018   **7.** 0.035   **11.** 0.042
4. 0.000 56   **8.** 4.8   **12.** 0.72

13. 0.84   **15.** 8.1   **17.** 0.077
14. 0.036   **16.** 0.0088   **18.** 0.28

19. 0.1502   **23.** 240   **27.** 22.4
20. 1.6   **24.** 63   **28.** 0.0022
21. 1.4   **25.** 0.112   **29.** 0.03
22. 0.000 912   **26.** 2.048   **30.** 0.01408

31. 0.64   **35.** 6.4   **39.** 0.64
32. 0.8   **36.** 0.08   **40.** 0.008
33. 0.64   **37.** 0.000 000 006 4   **41.** 0.0432
34. 0.0008   **38.** 800   **42.** 12.4

EXERCISE 6c
(p. 95)
1. 6.72   **5.** 434   **9.** 7476
2. 12.48   **6.** 0.4536   **10.** 118.4
3. 0.0952   **7.** 33   **11.** 8.97
4. 1253.2   **8.** 0.000 278 8   **12.** 198

13. 64.8   **17.** 2.56   **21.** 1.722
14. 0.111 52   **18.** 2.56   **22.** 17.29
15. 0.002 592   **19.** 0.0784   **23.** 22.96
16. 2.56   **20.** 0.1054   **24.** 0.031 02

EXERCISE 6d
(p. 96)
1. £325   **3.** 3.8 kg   **5.** 4216 p or £42.16   **7.** 3.25 m
2. 4.4 cm   **4.** 16.8 cm   **6.** 0.24   **8.** 50.4 m

Recurring decimals: not necessary at this stage and can well be omitted with average ability pupils.

EXERCISE 6e
(p. 97)
For above average pupils only.

1. 0.233... 0.2$\dot{3}$ **4.** 0.143 33... 0.14$\dot{3}$
2. 0.002 727... 0.00$\dot{2}\dot{7}$ **5.** 0.004 285 714 28... 0.004 285 7$\dot{1}$
3. 0.571 428 571... 0.$\dot{5}$71 42$\dot{8}$ **6.** 0.1222... 0.1$\dot{2}$

7. 0.444... 0.$\dot{4}$ **10.** 0.714 285 714... 0.$\dot{7}$14 28$\dot{5}$
8. 0.666... 0.$\dot{6}$ **11.** 0.777... 0.$\dot{7}$
9. 0.1818... 0.$\dot{1}\dot{8}$ **12.** 1.1428571428... 1.$\dot{1}$42857$\dot{}$

EXERCISE 6f
(p. 99)
Discussion about quantities that can be given exactly, quantities that cannot be given exactly (e.g. measurements), quantities that can be given exactly but often are not (e.g. government statistics) is useful here.

1. 0.33   **6.** 0.69   **11.** 14   **16.** 7
2. 0.32   **7.** 0.84   **12.** 6   **17.** 110
3. 1.27   **8.** 3.93   **13.** 27   **18.** 6
4. 2.35   **9.** 0.01   **14.** 3   **19.** 74
5. 0.04   **10.** 4.00   **15.** 4   **20.** 4

21. 0.363	**26.** 0.084	**31.** 1.8	**36.** 1.64
22. 0.026	**27.** 0.084	**32.** 42.6	**37.** 1.6
23. 0.007	**28.** 0.325	**33.** 1.01	**38.** 2
24. 0.070	**29.** 0.033	**34.** 0.0094	**39.** 3.50
25. 0.001	**30.** 4.000	**35.** 0.735	**40.** 3.5

EXERCISE 6g
(p. 100) Calculators should be used except by the brightest children who should use them only for checking answers. At this point they will need to be shown how to give an answer correct to a specified number of decimal places, by reading the display to one more place than necessary.

1. 0.17 (0.165)	**5.** 2.85 (3)	**9.** 0.24 (0.236)
2. 0.93 (0.927)	**6.** 0.16 (0.156)	**10.** 0.04 (0.038)
3. 0.35 (0.346)	**7.** 0.04 (2)	**11.** 0.22 (0.216)
4. 2.03 (3)	**8.** 0.05 (0.047)	**12.** 0.95 (0.949)

13. 4.1 (1)	**17.** 7.3 (7.29)	**21.** 9.7 (9.68)
14. 57.4 (2)	**18.** 1.2 (1.15)	**22.** 0.6 (4)
15. 2.6 (2.55)	**19.** 2.1 (4)	**23.** 1.7 (3)
16. 0.9 (0.88)	**20.** 0.9 (4)	**24.** 27.3 (1)

25. 0.006 (0.0057)	**29.** 0.038 (0.0375)	**33.** 0.016 (1)
26. 0.018 (0.0175)	**30.** 0.001 (0.0009)	**34.** 0.019 (0.0188)
27. 0.417 (0.4166)	**31.** 0.028 (4)	**35.** 0.039 (3)
28. 0.021 (0.0209)	**32.** 0.031 (0.0306)	**36.** 0.037 (0.0366)

EXERCISE 6h
(p. 101) Calculators should be used by all except the most able who can use them for checking.

1. 0.625	**3.** 0.1875	**5.** 0.36	**7.** 0.0625	**9.** 0.52
2. 0.075	**4.** 0.6	**6.** 0.14	**8.** 1.375	**10.** 0.0375

11. 0.429 (0.4285)	**18.** 0.111 (1)	**25.** 0.158 (0.1578)
12. 0.444 (4)	**19.** 0.333 (3)	**26.** 0.176 (4)
13. 0.167 (0.1666)	**20.** 0.364 (0.3636)	**27.** 0.267 (0.2666)
14. 0.667 (0.6666)	**21.** 0.214 (2)	**28.** 0.389 (0.3888)
15. 0.818 (1)	**22.** 0.235 (2)	**29.** 0.136 (3)
16. 0.857 (1)	**23.** 0.462 (0.4615)	**30.** 0.121 (2)
17. 1.143 (1.1428)	**24.** 0.190 (4)	

Division by decimals: much class discussion is necessary before pupils are asked to work on their own.

EXERCISE 6i
(p. 102) Nos. 1–24 do not need a calculator. Nos. 25–36: benefit will be obtained from using a calculator but pupils need to be shown how to get an estimate.

1. 0.2	**5.** 4500	**9.** 60
2. 0.02	**6.** 12	**10.** 5
3. 8	**7.** 0.16	**11.** 13
4. 20	**8.** 6	**12.** 120

13. 800
14. 360
15. 0.012
16. 0.01

17. 100
18. 2.3
19. 21
20. 0.012

21. 0.001 71
22. 52 000
23. 0.004
24. 60

25. 0.8
26. 900
27. 0.31
28. 0.16

29. 24.5
30. 3.2
31. 1.2
32. 41

33. 7
34. 1.2
35. 9
36. 0.08

EXERCISE 6j
(p. 103)

Unless long division practice is required, all pupils should use a calculator.

1. 6.33 (3)
2. 8.43 (8.428)
3. 16.67 (16.666)
4. 28.17 (28.165)
5. 0.72 (3)

6. 41.67 (41.666)
7. 0.03 (0.026)
8. 0.93 (0.928)
9. 1.03 (1.028)
10. 0.71 (4)

11. 0.02 (0)
12. 2.9 (2.87)
13. 8.2 (8.18)
14. 0.087 (0.0866)
15. 1.3333 (3)

16. 32.9 (32.85)
17. 20.3 (20.25)
18. 0.032 (3)
19. 283.333 (3)
20. 1.7 (1)

21. 36 (35.5)
22. 3.9 (3.86)
23. 0.167 (0.1666)
24. 1.1 (1.09)
25. 2.3 (2.28)

26. 4 (3.7)
27. 0.72 (3)
28. 0.0042 (0.004 15)
29. 0.57 (1)
30. 2.5 (2.47)

EXERCISE 6k
(p. 104)

Calculators can be used, the brightest pupils using them only for checking.

1. 0.144
2. 1.6

3. 0.0512
4. 128

5. 2.88
6. 5.76

7. 0.000 126
8. 0.14

9. 6.72
10. 4.2

11. 12.24
12. 84

13. 0.3
14. 0.16
15. 4

16. 4
17. 10
18. 0.12

19. 0.125
20. 0.7
21. 12

EXERCISE 6l
(p. 105)

Calculators should be used, except possibly by the most able.

1. 0.2, $\frac{1}{4}$
2. $\frac{2}{5}$, $\frac{4}{9}$
3. $\frac{4}{9}$, $\frac{1}{2}$
4. $\frac{3}{11}$, 0.3, $\frac{1}{3}$

5. $\frac{7}{8}$, $\frac{8}{9}$, 0.9
6. $\frac{3}{4}$, $\frac{17}{20}$
7. 0.35, $\frac{9}{25}$, $\frac{3}{8}$
8. $\frac{4}{7}$, 0.59, $\frac{3}{5}$

9. $\frac{3}{7}$, $\frac{5}{11}$, $\frac{6}{13}$
10. $\frac{8}{11}$, 0.7
11. 0.$\dot{3}$, $\frac{5}{12}$
12. 0.45, $\frac{9}{19}$, $\frac{1}{2}$

EXERCISE 6m
(p. 106)

1. a) 6.8   b) 680
2. 0.875
3. a) 3.13 b) 0.08 c) 3.00
4. 20.138
5. 4.48
6. 1.64
7. 11.82
8. $6\frac{2}{3}$; ($6\frac{2}{3}$ = 6.666...)

EXERCISE 6n
(p. 106)

1. $\frac{3}{50}$
2. a) 0.0624 b) 0.52
3. 1.7
4. 6.4 cm
5. 0.048
6. 0.24
7. £55.68
8. a) 8   b) 7.8   c) 7.782

EXERCISE 6p **1.** 0.$\dot{7}1428\dot{5}$ **3.** 16.28   **5.** 7.4437   **7.** $\frac{7}{9}$
(p. 107)   **2.** 0.064, 0.00064 **4.** $\frac{31}{50}$ **6.** 2.05   **8.** 25

EXERCISE 6q **1.** 0.16   **3.** 0.0036   **5.** 14.63   **7.** 2
(p. 107)   **2.** 9.186 (9.1857) **4.** $\frac{19}{2000}$ **6.** 59.5 p   **8.** 0.666...

CHAPTER 7 Units

Calculators are not necessary for this chapter.

EXERCISE 7a A good opportunity to point out the importance of eyes being directly over
(p. 108)   each end of a line when using a ruler to measure its length.

1. a) metres   b) centimetres   c) metres   d) kilometres
e) centimetres f) millimetres

3. a) 4 b) 2 c) 5 d) 1 e) 10

4. (to the nearest millimetre) a) 20 b) 10 c) 4 d) 16 e) 24

9. 40 cm

10. 900 cm

EXERCISE 7b **1.** 200   **5.** 12 000   **9.** 3000
(p. 110)   **2.** 5000   **6.** 150   **10.** 2 000 000
3. 30   **7.** 6000   **11.** 500
4. 400   **8.** 100 000   **12.** 7000

13. 150   **17.** 1900   **21.** 38
14. 23   **18.** 3500   **22.** 9200
15. 4600   **19.** 270   **23.** 2300
16. 3700   **20.** 190 000   **24.** 840

EXERCISE 7c **1.** 12 000   **5.** 1 000 000   **9.** 4000
(p. 111)   **2.** 3000   **6.** 13 000   **10.** 2 000 000
3. 5000   **7.** 6000   **11.** 3000
4. 1 000 000 **8.** 2 000 000   **12.** 4000

13. 1500   **17.** 5 200 000   **21.** 7300
14. 2700   **18.** 600   **22.** 300 000
15. 1800   **19.** 11 300   **23.** 500
16. 700   **20.** 2500   **24.** 800

EXERCISE 7d **1.** 136   **6.** 3020   **11.** 3500   **16.** 1020
(p. 112)   **2.** 35   **7.** 502   **12.** 2008   **17.** 1250
3. 1050   **8.** 5500   **13.** 5500   **18.** 3550
4. 48   **9.** 202   **14.** 2800   **19.** 2050
5. 207   **10.** 8009   **15.** 3250   **20.** 1010

EXERCISE 7e
(p. 112)

1. 30	**6.** 0.072	**11.** 1.5	**16.** 0.086
2. 6	**7.** 0.12	**12.** 3.68	**17.** 0.56
3. 1.5	**8.** 8.8	**13.** 1.5	**18.** 0.028
4. 25	**9.** 1.25	**14.** 5.02	**19.** 0.19
5. 1.6	**10.** 2.85	**15.** 3.8	**20.** 0.086

21. 3.45	**26.** 5.03	**31.** 5.142	**36.** 4.111
22. 8.4	**27.** 7.005	**32.** 48.171	**37.** 1.056
23. 11.002	**28.** 4.005	**33.** 9.008	**38.** 5.003
24. 2.042	**29.** 1.0001	**34.** 9.088	**39.** 0.2505
25. 4.4	**30.** 0.000 085	**35.** 12.019	**40.** 0.85055

EXERCISE 7f
(p. 114)

Worth pointing out to those of above average ability that, in the worked examples, part (b) can be obtained directly from part (a).

1. 5.86	**4.** 3051	**7.** 440	**10.** 2456
2. 1.035	**5.** 5.647	**8.** 55	**11.** 5059
3. 3001.36	**6.** 4.65	**9.** 1820	**12.** 1358

13. 3250	**16.** 2550	**19.** 2580	**22.** 1606.4
14. 5115	**17.** 1046.68	**20.** 2362	**23.** 1089.6
15. 15 100	**18.** 308.73	**21.** 2.22	**24.** 5972

25. 748	**30.** 19 850
26. 0.922	**31.** 35 420
27. 1150	**32.** 910
28. 73.6	**33.** 448.2
29. 2642	**34.** 5

EXERCISE 7g
(p. 115)

For the above average.

1. 13 540	**3.** 13.563	**5.** 32	**7.** 15 366	**9.** 22.77
2. 45 792	**4.** 12.55	**6.** 10.6	**8.** 24.448	**10.** 16.24

EXERCISE 7h
(p. 116)

Those of average ability would benefit from using a calculator.

1. 9.72 m	**3.** 748 kg	**5.** 1080 mm	**7.** 2.2 g	**9.** 33.2 cm
2. 1840 g	**4.** 4.11 g	**6.** 4 kg	**8.** 15 m	**10.** 5.3 kg

EXERCISE 7i
(p. 117)

1. 700 c	**6.** 4381 c	**11.** £1.26	**16.** £2.83
2. 600 p	**7.** 1103 pf	**12.** $3.50	**17.** 3.47 marks
3. 800 pf	**8.** 615 p	**13.** £1.90	**18.** £5.80
4. 1300 c	**9.** 210 p	**14.** 3.50 marks	**19.** 11.09 f
5. 735 c	**10.** 504 p	**15.** $43.07	**20.** £6.08

21. £3.20
22. $5.05
23. £9.60
24. 6 marks
25. £2.80

EXERCISE 7j
(p. 118) For the above average.

1. a) 98 cm   b) 980 mm
2. 2.23 km
3. 9.192 kg
4. 3056 m, 3050 m
5. 3.6 m
6. 95 t 660 kg;   121 t 960 kg
7. 76.9 kg,   72 kg
8. 13 360 m,   13.64 km
9. a) 6.2, 3.8   b) 620, 380
10. £6.75

EXERCISE 7k
(p. 119)

1. 4000 m
2. 0.03 kg
3. 350 cm
4. 0.25 kg
5. 3000 cm
6. 1.25 km
7. 1.5 m
8. 28 mm
9. 0.065 kg
10. 4.29 kg

EXERCISE 7l
(p. 120)

1. 2.36 m
2. 20 mm
3. 5000 g
4. 0.5 g
5. 4.25 km
6. 3600 kg
7. 2.35 kg
8. 2000 mg
9. 2.6 m

EXERCISE 7m
(p. 120)

1. 5780 kg
2. 354 p
3. 0.35 t
4. 0.0155 cm
5. 1.56 t
6. 7.80 f
7. 360 mg
8. 2.05 km
9. 8.598 t

EXERCISE 7n
(p. 120)

1. 4.2 cm
2. 0.35 kg
3. £1.52
4. 0.283 km
5. 3.6 cm
6. 470 mm
7. 0.36 m
8. 1.356 g
9. £7

CHAPTER 8   Imperial Units

As imperial units are still widely used, knowledge of them and of their rough equivalents in the metric system is desirable.

EXERCISE 8a
(p. 121)

1. 68 in
2. 14 ft
3. 1809 yd
4. 35 in
5. 100 in
6. 4320 yd
7. 17 ft
8. 123 in
9. 28 ft
10. 118 in
11. 3 ft
12. 2 ft 5 in
13. 7 ft 2 in
14. 3 yd
15. 4 yd 1 ft
16. 1 mile 240 yd
17. 6 ft 3 in
18. 33 yd 1 ft
19. 10 ft
20. 17 miles 80 yd

EXERCISE 8b
(p. 122)

1. 38 oz
2. 28 oz
3. 67 oz
4. 64 cwt
5. 162 lb
6. 1 lb 8 oz
7. 1 lb 2 oz
8. 2 lb 4 oz
9. 1 ton 10 cwt
10. 1 cwt 8 lb

EXERCISE 8c
(p. 123)

1. 6 lb
2. 6 ft
3. 2 kg
4. 3 m
5. 3 lb
6. 15 ft
7. 7 lb
8. $2\frac{1}{2}$ m
9. 8 oz
10. 1 lb

| **11.** 16 km | **13.** 24 km | **15.** 120 km |
| **12.** 32 km | **14.** 160 km | **16.** 64 km |

17. 11 lb	**21.** 1st cloth	**25.** 4 in
18. 2 m	**22.** 270 km	**26.** a) 25 mm b) 15 mm
19. 2 m	**23.** 8 oz	**27.** 15 cm
20. 4 kg	**24.** 15 cm	**28.** in the market

CHAPTER 9 Introducing Geometry

In all the geometry chapters there are no instructions as to how the solutions to problems should be written down. An intuitive approach is best at this age and most pupils should be asked only to fill in the sizes of angles in diagrams. The teacher will decide whether or not brighter children should be asked to write down reasoned solutions.

EXERCISE 9a
(p. 125)

1. $\frac{3}{4}$	**6.** $\frac{1}{2}$	**11.** $\frac{1}{3}$	**16.** 6	**21.** 6
2. $\frac{1}{2}$	**7.** $\frac{1}{2}$	**12.** $\frac{1}{3}$	**17.** 9	**22.** 4
3. $\frac{1}{4}$	**8.** $\frac{1}{2}$	**13.** $\frac{3}{4}$	**18.** 9	**23.** 8
4. $\frac{1}{2}$	**9.** 1	**14.** $\frac{3}{4}$	**19.** 3	**24.** 9
5. $\frac{1}{4}$	**10.** $\frac{1}{4}$	**15.** $\frac{2}{3}$	**20.** 6	**25.** 12

EXERCISE 9b
(p. 127)

| **1.** N | **3.** N | **5.** N | **7.** $\frac{3}{4}$ |
| **2.** W | **4.** E No | **6.** $\frac{3}{4}$ | **8.** $\frac{1}{2}$ |

EXERCISE 9c
(p. 128)

1. 1	**5.** 4	**9.** 2	**13.** 4
2. 2	**6.** 2	**10.** 1	
3. 3	**7.** 3	**11.** 1	
4. 1	**8.** 4	**12.** 3	

EXERCISE 9d
(p. 129)

| **1.** obtuse | **3.** reflex | **5.** obtuse |
| **2.** acute | **4.** acute | **6.** reflex |

7. acute	**10.** acute	**13.** obtuse
8. acute	**11.** reflex	**14.** obtuse
9. obtuse	**12.** obtuse	**15.** acute

EXERCISE 9e
(p. 130)

Worth discussing the number 360, e.g. how many whole numbers divide exactly into it? Compare it with 100; which is the better number and why? Its origins are interesting: it probably came from the Babylonians who used 60 as a number base. It is also worth noting that 60 is the base used for time (seconds and minutes and hours).

| **1.** 180° | **2.** 90° | **3.** 270° |

4. 180° **8.** 270° **12.** 270°
5. 90° **9.** 90° **13.** 180°
6. 270° **10.** 120° **14.** 90°
7. 180° **11.** 270° **15.** 180°

16. 30° **21.** 30° **26.** 210° **31.** 210°
17. 45° **22.** 120° **27.** 180° **32.** 300°
18. 120° **23.** 30° **28.** 300° **33.** 210°
19. 60° **24.** 60° **29.** 330° **34.** 150°
20. 45° **25.** 120° **30.** 150° **35.** 210°

EXERCISE 9f **1.** 34° **3.** 75° **5.** 150° **7.** 115° **9.** 80°
(p. 132) **2.** 60° **4.** 137° **6.** 20° **8.** 54° **10.** 11°

11. 325° **12.** 332° **13.** 250° **14.** 218° **15.** 345°

16. 330° **18.** 345° **20.** 213°
17. 240° **19.** 282° **21.** 145°

EXERCISE 9g Intended to give pupils an idea of what an angle of given size looks like.
(p. 136)
1. 30° **3.** 90° **5.** 150°
2. 60° **4.** 120° **6.** 180°

7. 3 **11.** 5 **15.** 2 **19.** 6
8. 2 **12.** 9 **16.** 6 **20.** 8
9. 4 **13.** 1 **17.** 3 **21.** 1
10. 12 **14.** 10 **18.** 7 **22.** 12

35. 60° **38.** 260° **41.** 45° **44.** 80°
36. 140° **39.** 25° **42.** 5° **45.** 160°
37. 350° **40.** 300° **43.** 25° **46.** 105°

EXERCISE 9h If pupils do measure each other's angles, it is worth pointing out that
(p. 138) protractors are not always as accurate as they should be; an angle measured
as 51° on one protractor could be measured as 52° on another.

EXERCISE 9i In No. 3 check that the pupils' diagrams vary.
(p. 138)
4. 150° **6.** 35° **8.** 140°
5. 20° **7.** 65° **9.** 160°

EXERCISE 9j No. 1, or a similar one, could be demonstrated by one of the children in front
(p. 140) of the class.

1. 180° **2.** 180°

EXERCISE 9k **1.** 120° **5.** 20° **9.** 135°
(p. 140) **2.** 155° **6.** 130° **10.** 140°
3. 10° **7.** 80° **11.** 90°
4. 100° **8.** 15° **12.** 50°

13. *e* & *f*   **16.** *f* & *g*
14. *m* & *k*, *j* & *d*   **17.** *f* & *g*, *g* & *d*, *d* & *e*, *e* & *f*
15. *d* & *f*, *f* & *e*, *e* & *g*, *g* & *d*   **18.** *n* & *d*, *d* & *p*, *p* & *m*, *m* & *n*

19. 50°, 130°, 130°   **23.** 45°, 135°, 135°
20. 60°, 120°, 120°   **24.** 180°, 155°
21. 180°, 60°   **25.** 80°, 100°, 100°
22. 105°, 180°   **26.** 165°, 180°

EXERCISE 9l   **1.** 110°   **6.** 150°
(p. 144)   **2.** 60°   **7.** 100°
                  3. 110°   **8.** 120°
                  4. 80°   **9.** 310°
                  5. 180°   **10.** 60°

EXERCISE 9m   **1.** 120°   **4.** 310°   **7.** 40°
(p. 145)   **2.** 120°, 60°   **5.** 150°, 60°   **8.** 120°, 60°, 120°, 60°
                  3. 120°   **6.** 50°

EXERCISE 9n   **1.** 240°   **3.** 20°   **4.** 145°   **5.** 140°   **6.** 140°
(p. 146)

EXERCISE 9p   **1.** 240°   **3.** 354°   **5.** 50°
(p. 146)   **2.** W   **4.** 140°, 40° **6.** 30°

CHAPTER 10   Symmetry

This chapter can be done earlier, but should be done before Chapter 11.

EXERCISE 10a   1, 3, 4 and 6
(p. 148)

EXERCISE 10b **1.** 2   **2.** 1   **3.** 0   **4.** 1   **5.** 2   **6.** 2
(p. 150)

EXERCISE 10c **1.** 6   **2.** 6   **3.** 0   **4.** 3
(p. 152)

EXERCISE 10d It is advisable to point out that the amount of rotation must not be a
(p. 153)   complete revolution.

                  2, 3 and 5.

                  9. In Exercise 10c, numbers 1, 2, 3, 4, 7 and 8 have rotational symmetry.

EXERCISE 10e **1.** yes   **5.** yes
(p. 155)   **2.** no   **6.** yes
                  3. yes   **7.** no
                  4. yes   **8.** yes

EXERCISE 10f **1.**
(p. 156)

2.

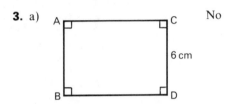

3. a) A 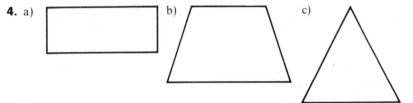 C No b) rectangle

4. a)   b)   c)

EXERCISE 10g **1.** yes
(p. 158) **2.** no
3. yes
4. yes

5. yes
6. no
7. e.g. saucepan, milk bottle

CHAPTER 11   Triangles and Angles

Angles of a triangle: some teachers may prefer to use paper tearing *before* drawing and measurement of angles. This applies also to angles of a quadrilateral later in the chapter.

EXERCISE 11c
(p. 163)

1. 60°	**6.** 30°	**11.** 50°
2. 85°	**7.** 55°	**12.** 90°
3. 55°	**8.** 60°	**13.** 120°
4. 110°	**9.** 75°	**14.** 55°
5. 40°	**10.** 25°	**15.** 65°

EXERCISE 11d   **1.** 60°, 50°   **4.** 65°, 115°   **7.** 60°
(p. 164)   **2.** 65°, 45°   **5.** 85°, 30°   **8.** 60°, 30°
                   3. 70°   **6.** 45°   **9.** 90°, 45°

EXERCISE 11e   **1.** 110°   **3.** 70°   **5.** 70°   **7.** 90°   **9.** 110°
(p. 166)   **2.** 60°   **4.** 40°   **6.** 55°   **8.** 35°   **10.** 95°

EXERCISE 11f Some of the remaining measurements of each constructed triangle are given
(p. 168)   here and in the following exercises to help check pupils' drawings.
                 Alternatively the children can be asked to find them from their own drawings.

   1. 4.2 cm, 56°, 84°   **6.** 4.8 cm, 79°, 53°
   2. 4.6 cm, 97°, 48°   **7.** 4.3 cm, 53°, 62°
   3. 6.5 cm, 70°, 40°   **8.** 5.7 cm, 53°, 75°
   4. 8.5 cm, 97°, 33°   **9.** 6.4 cm, 38°, 69°
   5. 3.8 cm, 52°, 83°   **10.** 6.2 cm, 44°, 80°

EXERCISE 11g   **1.** 34°, 106°   **6.** 45°, 83°
(p. 169)   **2.** 34°, 98°   **7.** 37°, 90°
                   3. 35°, 80°   **8.** 47°, 75°
                   4. 37°, 90°   **9.** 23°, 90°
                   5. 40°, 84°   **10.** 52°, 69°

EXERCISE 11h   **1.** 3.6 cm, 5.4 cm   **6.** 13.4 cm, 17.8 cm
(p. 169)   **2.** 34°, 101°   **7.** 8.9 cm, 30°
                   3. 4.6 cm, 49°   **8.** 5.9 cm, 5 cm
                   4. 7.8 cm, 50°   **9.** 127°, 21°
                   5. 119°, 26°   **10.** Equilateral

   11. Two possible triangles: $\hat{C} = 56°$, $b = 6$ cm; $\hat{C} = 124°$, $b = 2.6$ cm
   12. $\hat{R} = 71°$, $q = 4.8$ cm; $\hat{R} = 109°$, $q = 1.2$ cm
   13. 35°, 2.9 cm;   no

EXERCISE 11i   **1.** 50°   **6.** 40°   **11.** 110°   **14.** 80°, 70°
(p. 171)   **2.** 80°   **7.** 90°   **12.** 65°   **15.** 80°, 115°
                   3. 110°   **8.** 60°   **13.** 60°, 120°   **16.** 50°, 130°
                   4. 50°   **9.** 120°
                   5. 60°   **10.** 90°

EXERCISE 11j   **11.** 70°   **14.** 40°   **17.** 45°   **20.** 20°
(p. 174)   **12.** 70°   **15.** 90°   **18.** 70°   **21.** 75°
                   13. 65°   **16.** 110°   **19.** 60°   **22.** 86°

                   27. 55°, 70°   **30.** 50°, 80°
                   28. 45°, 135°   **31.** 40°, 140°
                   29. 80°, 80°   **32.** 20°, 70°

EXERCISE 11k In No. 6, two tetrahedra can be stuck together to make a polyhedron with six
(p. 177) faces. The nets for other simple polyhedra are provided in Book 2 but are not
included here because at this stage constructions are rarely accurate enough to
give satisfying results.

EXERCISE 11l **1.** 65°   **3.** 80°   **5.** 10 cm
(p. 178) **2.** 70°   **4.** AC = 3.9 cm

EXERCISE 11m **1.** 85°, 45°   **3.** 55°, 125°   **5.** AC = 4.1 cm
(p. 179) **2.** 45°, 135°   **4.** $\hat{C}$ = 70°

EXERCISE 11n **1.** 60°, 30°   **3.** 80°, 140°   **5.** 96°, 136°, 58°
(p. 180) **2.** 65°, 65°, 60°   **4.** 7.1 cm (base)

CHAPTER 12 Factors and Indices

EXERCISE 12a **1.** 1×18, 2×9, 3×6
(p. 181) **2.** 1×20, 2×10, 4×5
3. 1×24, 2×12, 3×8, 4×6
4. 1×27, 3×9
5. 1×30, 2×15, 3×10, 5×6
6. 1×36, 2×18, 3×12, 4×9, 6×6
7. 1×40, 2×20, 4×10, 5×8
8. 1×45, 3×15, 5×9
9. 1×48, 2×24, 3×16, 4×12, 6×8
10. 1×60, 2×30, 3×20, 4×15, 5×12, 6×10
11. 1×64, 2×32, 4×16, 8×8
12. 1×72, 2×36, 3×24, 4×18, 6×12, 8×9
13. 1×80, 2×40, 4×20, 5×16, 8×10
14. 1×96, 2×48, 3×32, 4×24, 6×16, 8×12
15. 1×100, 2×50, 4×25, 5×20, 10×10
16. 1×108, 2×54, 3×36, 4×27, 6×18, 9×12
17. 1×120, 2×60, 3×40, 4×30, 5×24, 6×20, 8×15, 10×12
18. 1×135, 3×45, 5×27, 9×15
19. 1×144, 2×72, 3×48, 4×36, 6×24, 8×18, 9×16, 12×12
20. 1×160, 2×80, 4×40, 5×32, 8×20, 10×16

EXERCISE 12b Some examples discussed with the class would be useful.
(p. 181)
1. 21, 24, 27, 30, 33, 36, 39   **4.** 55, 66, 77, 88, 99
2. 20, 25, 30, 35, 40, 45   **5.** 26, 39, 52, 65
3. 28, 35, 42, 49, 56

EXERCISE 12c **1.** 2, 3, 5, 7, 11, 13   **4.** 5, 19, 29, 61
(p. 181) **2.** 23, 29   **5.** 41, 101, 127
3. 31, 37, 41, 43, 47   **6.** a) F b) F c) T d) T e) F

EXERCISE 12d
(p. 182)

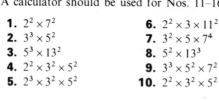

1. 2^3
2. 3^4
3. 5^4
4. 7^5
5. 2^5
6. 3^6
7. 13^3
8. 19^2
9. 2^7
10. 6^4

11. 32
12. 27
13. 25
14. 8
15. 9
16. 49
17. 81
18. 16

19. 2^2
20. 3^2
21. 2^3
22. 3^3
23. 7^2
24. 5^2
25. 2^5
26. 2^6

EXERCISE 12e A calculator should be used for Nos. 11–16.
(p. 183)

1. $2^2 \times 7^2$
2. $3^3 \times 5^2$
3. $5^3 \times 13^2$
4. $2^2 \times 3^2 \times 5^2$
5. $2^3 \times 3^2 \times 5^2$
6. $2^2 \times 3 \times 11^2$
7. $3^2 \times 5 \times 7^4$
8. $5^2 \times 13^3$
9. $3^3 \times 5^2 \times 7^2$
10. $2^2 \times 3^2 \times 5^2$

11. 108
12. 225
13. 112
14. 36
15. 180
16. 126

EXERCISE 12f
(p. 184)

1. yes
2. no
3. yes
4. yes
5. no
6. yes
7. yes
8. no
9. yes
10. yes
11. yes

EXERCISE 12g
(p. 185)

1. $2^3 \times 3$
2. $2^2 \times 7$
3. $3^2 \times 7$
4. $2^3 \times 3^2$
5. $2^3 \times 17$
6. $2^2 \times 3 \times 7$
7. $2^3 \times 3^3$
8. $2^4 \times 3 \times 11$
9. $3^4 \times 5$
10. $2^4 \times 7^2$

EXERCISE 12h
(p. 185)

1. 3
2. 8
3. 12
4. 14
5. 25
6. 11
7. 21
8. 13
9. 5
10. 4
11. 15
12. 2

EXERCISE 12i
(p. 186)

1. 15
2. 24
3. 15
4. 36
5. 36
6. 60
7. 48
8. 60
9. 36
10. 108
11. 36
12. 168

EXERCISE 12j These problems are difficult and should be approached with caution. They are
(p. 186) useful for discussion but only the most able children should be allowed to
work through them on their own.

1. £1
2. £10.80
3. 120 m
4. 50 cm
5. 2 minutes past midnight
6. 78 s
7. 13 turns and 6 turns
8. 30 steps; 2
9. 3 minutes
10. 480, 20

CHAPTER 13 **Tables and Networks**

EXERCISE 13a
(p. 188)

1. a) £19.20   b) £18.60   c) £35.30
  d) London, Saturday + Alton Towers, weekday, or Birmingham, Sunday + Alton Towers, Saturday
2. a) £49 b) £61 c) £6000, in Area 3   d) £6000 in Area 1 or £7000 in Area 2
  e) £6000, in Area 2   f) Martins £7000, Barkers £6000

EXERCISE 13b
(p. 190)

Many other questions can be asked about these tables.

1. a) 4   b) 15   c) 22   d) 32
  e) Otherwise there is no-one to be in the class
2. a) 1   b) 15   c) 30
3. a) 9   b) 1   c) 14   d) 28   e) 23
4. a) Missing numbers are 4 and 9   b) 9   c) 3

Other tables can be made to show information collected in the class.

EXERCISE 13c
(p. 192)

1. a) 14 km   b) 17 km   c) 22 km
  d) 21 km   e) e.g. A to E to D to C, 24 km   f) via F
2. a) 550 m   b) 440 m   c) 705 m
3. a) 790 m   b) yes, between church and school
                and between Post Office and school
4. a) Post Office, shop, school, Daisy's house, school, Post Office; 560 m
  b) Post Office, school, Daisy's house, school, Post Office, Pete's house, Post Office or this route in reverse; 820 m
5. a) 12 m   b) 33 m   c) 60 m
  d) A to C to D, 32 m   e) A to B to D, 33 m
6. a) 10 min   b) 35 min
  c) A to D to E to B, 30 min   d) B to E to D, 25 min

EXERCISE 13d
(p. 194)

1. drawing is possible starting at B but not at C
3. (a) and (b) are not possible
4. a) B, F, I, K, L, M
  b) points other than those in (a)
6. Diagrams with only even numbers can be drawn starting at any point. Diagrams with two odd numbers can be drawn starting from one of the odd points. Other diagrams cannot be drawn.

EXERCISE 13e
(p. 196)

1. a) AEI 6, ADGHEI 24, ADEFI 17, ABCEFI 17, ABEI 8, ADGHEFI 28, ADGEFI 23
  b) ADGHEFI
2. a) ABC, 10 min
  b) ABEADC, 38 min
  c) 24 min
3. a) Yes, from P, finishing at C
     Yes, from C, finishing at P. Not possible from any other point.
  b) no
4. a) yes   b) yes   c) no

EXERCISE 13f **1.**
(p. 198)

To

		A	B	C	D
	A	0	1	2	0
	B	0	0	1	0
From	C	2	1	0	1
	D	0	0	1	0

2. a)

To

		A	B	C
	A	0	2	1
From	B	2	0	2
	C	1	2	0

b)

To

		A	B	C	D
	A	0	1	0	1
	B	1	0	1	1
From	C	0	1	0	1
	D	1	2	1	0

c)

To

		A	B
	A	2	2
From	B	2	0

3.

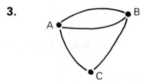   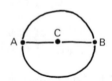

The table is symmetrical about the leading diagonal (i.e. top left to bottom right).

4. a)

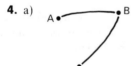

c)

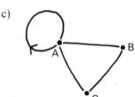

b)

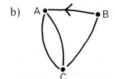

d)

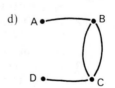

There are other possible maps, as in question 3.

EXERCISE 13g **1.** a) David   b) no, son   c) sister   d) grandfather   e) aunt
(p. 200)

2. a) Sally   b) older   c) we do not know
d)   Ian   e)   Ian

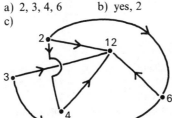

3. a) 2, 3, 4, 6   b) yes, 2
c)

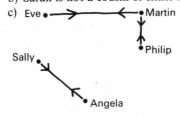

4. a) the relationship works both ways   b) yes

5. a) Philip and Martin are cousins
b) Sarah is not a cousin of either Philip or Martin
c) Eve •——→   ←——• Martin
• Philip
Sally •
• Angela

CHAPTER 14   Area

Plenty of class discussion is advisable before finding areas of specific objects:
e.g. What is "area"? Why is area counted in squares and not in triangles?
The number of squares may vary because it is not always easy to say whether more
than half a square is included.

EXERCISE 14a **1.** 11   **5.** 26   **9.** 45   **13.** 37
(p. 202)   **2.** 16   **6.** 20   **10.** 43   **14.** 76
3. 11   **7.** 21   **11.** 50   **15.** 62
4. 20   **8.** a) A b) B   **12.** 40   **16.** 26

EXERCISE 14b
(p. 206)

1. 4 cm^2
2. 64 cm^2
3. 100 cm^2
4. 25 cm^2
5. 2.25 cm^2
6. 6.25 cm^2
7. 0.49 m^2
8. 1.44 cm^2
9. $\frac{1}{4}$ km^2
10. $\frac{9}{16}$ m^2
11. 30 cm^2
12. 48 cm^2
13. 27 m^2
14. 280 cm^2
15. 3.96 mm^2
16. 1470 km^2
17. 2.85 m^2
18. 30.24 cm^2
19. 22 800 cm^2
20. 36 000 mm^2

EXERCISE 14c
(p. 207)

1. 120 cm^2
2. 36 m^2
3. 149 m^2
4. 208 mm^2
5. 52 m^2
6. 87 cm^2
7. 544 mm^2
8. 90 cm^2
9. 43 m^2
10. 228 cm^2

EXERCISE 14d
(p. 209)

1. 8 cm
2. 32 cm
3. 40 cm
4. 20 cm
5. 6 cm
6. 10 cm
7. 2.8 m
8. 4.8 cm
9. 2 km
10. 3 m
11. 22 cm
12. 28 cm
13. 24 m
14. 68 cm
15. 8 mm
16. 154 km
17. 6.8 m
18. 22.2 cm
19. 670 cm
20. 780 mm

EXERCISE 14e
(p. 209)

1. 2 cm, 8 cm^2
2. 2 cm, 10 cm^2
3. 5 m, 15 m^2
4. 9 mm, 54 mm^2
5. 5 cm, 22 cm
6. 12 m, 44 m
7. 9 km, 26 km
8. 9 mm, 32 mm
9. 25 cm, 125 cm^2
10. 80 cm, 202 cm

EXERCISE 14f
(p. 210)

Intended for the above average.

1. 28 cm^2, 24 cm
2. 24 cm^2, 24 cm
3. 80 mm^2, 48 cm
4. 15 m^2, 32 cm
5. 1664 cm^2, 272 cm
6. 184 cm^2
7. 91 cm^2
8. 198 cm^2
9. 432 cm^2
10. 4.84 cm^2

EXERCISE 14g
(p. 212)

1. 4
2. 9
3. 6
4. 6
5. 45
6. 500

EXERCISE 14h
(p. 213)

1. a) 30 000   b) 120 000   c) 75 000   d) 820 000   e) 85 000
2. a) 1400   b) 300   c) 750   d) 2600   e) 3250
3. a) 560   b) 56 000
4. a) 4   b) 25   c) 0.5   d) 0.25   e) 7.34
5. a) 0.55   b) 14   c) 0.076   d) 1.86   e) 2970
6. a) 7.5   b) 0.43   c) 0.05   d) 0.245   e) 176

EXERCISE 14i Pupils will benefit from using a calculator.
(p. 215)

1. $50\,000\,cm^2$
2. $1800\,mm^2$
3. $175\,000\,cm^2$
4. $14\,000\,cm^2$
5. $8\,m^2$

6. $15\,000\,cm^2$
7. $37\,500\,cm^2$
8. $180\,mm^2$
9. $120\,000\,m^2$
10. $22\,500\,m^2$

EXERCISE 14j Average ability children should be encouraged to try some of these with the
(p. 215) help of a calculator.

1. $8250\,m^2$, $370\,m$
2. $7000\,m^2$, $340\,m$
3. $8400\,m^2$, $380\,m$
4. $312\,m^2$, $76\,m$
5. $5\,m^2$

6. 1200
7. £9
8. $9000\,cm^2$
9. 100
10. 96

CHAPTER 15   Parallel Lines and Angles

EXERCISE 15a Can be used for discussion.
(p. 217)

EXERCISE 15b   1. *g*   3. *d*   5. *f*   7. *d*   9. *e*
(p. 219)   2. *e*   4. *e*   6. *f*   8. *g*   10. *d*

EXERCISE 15d   1. 60°   4. 60°   7. 110°   10. 130°
(p. 222)   2. 110°   5. 60°   8. 120°   11. 130°
    3. 75°   6. 80°   9. 30°   12. 45°

EXERCISE 15e   1. 50°
(p. 224)   2. 130°, 130°, 50°
    3. 60°, 60°, 60°, 120°, 60°
    4. 50°, 80°, 50°

5. 70°, 80°, 30°
6. 115°, 115°
7. 140°, 40°, 40°
8. 70°, 110°, 70°, 70°

9. 50°, 45°, 50°
10. 55°, 125°, 55°
11. 110°, 70°, 130°, 130°
12. 40°, 100°
13. 80°

14. 90°, 90°, 50°
15. 120°
16. 40°
17. 70°
18. 60°

19. 135°
20. 55°
21. 55°

22. 120°
23. 120°
24. 45°

EXERCISE 15f   1. *e*   3. *d*   5. *d*   7. *g*   9. *d*
(p. 227)   2. *e*   4. *d*   6. *g*   8. *e*   10. *g*

EXERCISE 15g
(p. 229)
1. 50°, 130°
2. 130°, 50°
3. 50°, 70°
4. 260°, 40°, 60°

5. 70°, 70°, 70°
6. 45°, 90°
7. 55°, 65°
8. 60°

9. 90°
10. 90°
11. 30°
12. 45°

EXERCISE 15h
(p. 230)
1. *e*, *g*
2. *e*, *d*
3. *e*, *g*

4. *e*, *d*
5. *h*, *f*
6. *d*, *g*

7. 70°, 110°, 180°
8. 130°, 50°, 180°

9. 40°, 40°, 80°
10. 120°, 60°, 180°

EXERCISE 15i
(p. 232)
1. 120°
2. 130°, 50°
3. 85°
4. 40°, 100°, 60°
5. 55°, 125°

6. 40°
7. 80°, 80°
8. 130°, 130°, 50°
9. 80°, 100°, 80°, 100°
10. 70°, 110°

EXERCISE 15j
(p. 233)
1. 65°
2. 140°
3. 55°

4. 110°
5. 70°
6. 70°

7. 45°
8. 75°
9. parallel

EXERCISE 15k
(p. 234)
1. 80°
2. 60°

3. 110°
4. 40°

5. 25°
6. 50°

7. 40°
8. 40°

EXERCISE 15l
(p. 235)
1. 60°

2. 110°

3. 90°

4. 130°

CHAPTER 16   Coordinates

Negative numbers as coordinates are introduced in this chapter. Some teachers may prefer first to introduce negative numbers in general, in which case Chapter 17 should be taken before this one.

EXERCISE 16a Nos. 10–21 can be used for discussion.
(p. 237)

1. A (2,2), B (5,2), C (7,6), D (4,5), E (7,0), F (9,4), G (0,8), H (5,8)

4. square
5. isosceles triangle
6. rectangle

7. square
8. isosceles triangle

10. 5
11. 7
12. 0
13. 1
14. 14
15. 0

16. 5
17. 4
18. 1
19. 6
20. 5
21. 0

22. (9,12), (9,9), (13,6)
23. (3,11), (3,7), (7,7); 4
24. (1,1), (6,1), (8,4), (3,4); 5,5
25. (13,3); 4

26. (2,5)
27. (7,1)
28. (4,1)
29. (5,4)
30. (3,7)
31. (2,3)

EXERCISE 16b
(p. 241)
This and the next exercise use positive coordinates to investigate some of the properties of the special quadrilaterals. The questions are not difficult but this section can be omitted at a first reading.

    1. a) 8, 8, 8, 8 b) DC, yes c) 90°
    2. a) AB and DC, BC and AD b) AB and DC, BC and AD c) 90°
    3. a) all equal b) AB and DC, BC and AD c) $\hat{A}=\hat{C}$, $\hat{B}=\hat{D}$
    4. a) AB and DC, BC and AD b) AB and DC, BC and AD c) $\hat{A}=\hat{C}$, $\hat{B}=\hat{D}$
    5. a) none b) AB and DC c) none

EXERCISE 16c
(p. 243)

  1. parallelogram
  2. rectangle
  3. trapezium
  4. square
  5. trapezium

  6. rhombus
  7. square
  8. rectangle
  9. parallelogram
 10. rhombus

EXERCISE 16d
(p. 244)

  1. 2, 3, 6, 1, −5, −3, 5, −3, −5, 5, 0
  2. 2, −2, 5, −4, 2, 5, −5, 0

3. 5 below	**6.** 10 above	**9.** 3 right	**12.** 7 left
4. 3 above	**7.** on x-axis	**10.** 5 left	**13.** on y-axis
5. 1 below	**8.** 4 below	**11.** 2 right	**14.** 9 left

  15. A (−2,3), B (3,1), C (2,−2), D (−3,1), E (1,−4), F (−2,−2), G (−4,−4),
      H (1,2), I (4,−4), J (−4,3)

  18. square   **19.** isosceles triangle   **20.** rectangle   **21.** right-angled

EXERCISE 16e
(p. 247)

1. 6	**6.** 7
2. 8	**7.** 5
3. 6	**8.** 7
4. 2	**9.** 11
5. 2	**10.** 11

11. (−1,1)	**16.** (0,−1)	**21.** (4,2)	**26.** (4,$\frac{3}{2}$)
12. (1,−2)	**17.** (3,2)	**22.** (2,−1)	**27.** (−1,3)
13. (−1,3)	**18.** (−1,2)	**23.** (−$\frac{7}{2}$,3)	**28.** (−1,0)
14. (−6,−1)	**19.** (−1,3)	**24.** (−3,−1)	**29.** (0,0)
15. (−5,1)	**20.** (1,0)	**25.** (−5,−2)	**30.** (−1,0)

EXERCISE 16f Suitable for the above average only.
(p. 248)

    1. a) (1,2), (3,6), (−3,−6), (−2,−4), (2,4) b) 10 c) 16, 20, −8, 6, 9, −5, 2a
    2. a) (2,2), (4,3), (6,4), (10,6), (−4,−1), (−8,−3), (0,1)
       b) y-coordinate $= \frac{1}{2}(x$-coordinate$)+1$ c) 5
       d) 7, 11, 16, −5, 16, $\frac{1}{2}a+1$
    3. a) (3,−1), (5,−3), (6,−4), (8,−6), (−2,4), (−4,6), (1,1)
       b) −5, −8, −10, −18, 9, 11, −8, 10, −10

EXERCISE 16g Omit this exercise if Exercise 16b and Exercise 16c were not covered.
(p. 250)   This exercise investigates the properties of the diagonals of the special quadrilaterals and can be omitted, although the questions are not difficult.

1. a) parallelogram   c) no   d) both   e) no
2. a) square   c) yes   d) both   e) yes
3. a) trapezium   c) no   d) neither   e) no
4. a) rhombus   c) no   d) both   e) yes
5. a) rectangle   c) yes   d) both   e) no
6. rectangle, square
7. rhombus, square
8. parallelogram, rectangle, rhombus, square

EXERCISE 16h **1.** $(-4, 16)$ **3.** $(1, 1)$ **5.** $(2, 4)$
(p. 250)   **2.** $(-3, 9)$ **4.** $(0, 0)$ **6.** $(4, 16)$

7. ignoring the minus sign, the y coordinate is the square of the x coordinate

8. 9   **10.** 6.25   **12.** 2.7 (-2.7)
9. 4   **11.** 2.25

CHAPTER 17   Directed Numbers

EXERCISE 17a **1.** $+10°$ **4.** $+5°$ **7.** 2° below   **10.** 10° below
(p. 253)   **2.** $-7°$ **5.** $-8°$ **8.** 3° above   **11.** 8° above
                  3. $-3°$ **6.** $0°$ **9.** 4° above   **12.** freezing point

13. 10°   **18.** $-2°$
14. 12°   **19.** 1°
15. 4°   **20.** 3°
16. $-3°$ **21.** $-7°$
17. 2°   **22.** $-2°$

24. -5 s   **29.** $+£50$ **33.** $+200$ m   **37.** $+150$ m
25. $+5$ s   **30.** $-£5$ **34.** -5 m   **38.** $-3°$C
26. $+50$ p   **31.** $+5$ paces   **35.** $-3°$C   **39.** $+25$ p
27. -50 p   **32.** -5 paces   **36.** $+21°$C   **40.** 6 paces in front
28. -1 min

EXERCISE 17b **1.** $>$ **5.** $>$ **9.** $>$
(p. 256)   **2.** $>$ **6.** $<$ **10.** $<$
                  3. $>$ **7.** $>$ **11.** $<$
                  4. $<$ **8.** $>$ **12.** $>$

13. 10, 12   **17.** 0, -3 **21.** $\frac{1}{6}, \frac{1}{36}$
14. $-10, -12$ **18.** 5, 8   **22.** $-4, -2$
15. $-2, -4$ **19.** $-7, -11$ **23.** $-8, -16$
16. 2, 4   **20.** 16, 32   **24.** $-2, -3$

EXERCISE 17c **1.** −3   **6.** 7   **11.** 5   **14.** −1
(p. 257)   **2.** 3   **7.** 1   **12.** −2   **15.** −6
                 3. −2   **8.** 2   **13.** −2   **16.** 6
                 4. −2   **9.** −12
                 5. 2   **10.** −1

17. 2   **24.** −5   **31.** 1   **36.** −2
18. −3   **25.** 4   **32.** 2   **37.** 1
19. −3   **26.** 6   **33.** 2   **38.** 2
20. −1   **27.** 3   **34.** −2   **39.** 5
21. 3   **28.** 0   **35.** −1   **40.** 16
22. −6   **29.** −3
23. −10 **30.** −5

Addition and subtraction of negative numbers: discussion using many different examples is advisable.

EXERCISE 17d **1.** 2   **6.** 3   **11.** −14   **16.** 7   **21.** 13
(p. 259)   **2.** −3 **7.** −3   **12.** 0   **17.** −3   **22.** 13
                 3. 7   **8.** 6   **13.** 0   **18.** 2   **23.** −6
                 4. 3   **9.** −14 **14.** 6   **19.** −4   **24.** 8
                 5. −9 **10.** 10 **15.** −6   **20.** 5   **25.** 1

EXERCISE 17e **1.** 1   **9.** 15   **17.** −1   **24.** 19
(p. 260)   **2.** −5   **10.** 2   **18.** 0   **25.** −4
                 3. 9   **11.** 5   **19.** 2   **26.** −4
                 4. 8   **12.** −12 **20.** 16   **27.** 4
                 5. −12 **13.** 5   **21.** 5   **28.** −3
                 6. 7   **14.** −9   **22.** −4   **29.** −3
                 7. 4   **15.** 1   **23.** −8   **30.** −19
                 8. 10   **16.** 9

31. 2   **34.** 0   **37.** 9   **41.** −10
32. 3   **35.** −1   **38.** −7   **42.** −3
33. 0   **36.** 0   **39.** −4   **43.** −2
                       40. 3   **44.** 1

45. 2   **51.** 2
46. −12 **52.** −15
47. 3   **53.** −9
48. 18   **54.** −6
49. −2   **55.** −8
50. 1

EXERCISE 17f **1.** −24   **6.** −12   **11.** −16
(p. 261)   **2.** −14   **7.** −48   **12.** −36
                 3. −24   **8.** −5   **13.** −42
                 4. −12   **9.** −6   **14.** −5
                 5. −27   **10.** −5   **15.** −12.5

EXERCISE 17g	**1.** −3	**5.** −4	**9.** −5	**13.** −2	**17.** −4
(p. 262)	**2.** −2	**6.** −2	**10.** −4	**14.** −2	**18.** −2
	3. −5	**7.** −10	**11.** −1	**15.** −4	
	4. −4	**8.** −3	**12.** −2	**16.** −9	

EXERCISE 17h	**1.** −5°		**3.** 2		**7.** 0
(p. 263)	**2.** a) < b) >		**4.** −5		**8.** 5
			5. −2		**9.** −24
			6. 4		**10.** −12

EXERCISE 17i	**1.** −3°		**3.** −6		**7.** 0
(p. 263)	**2.** a) > b) >		**4.** −2		**8.** 3
			5. 5		**9.** −12
			6. 1		**10.** −2

CHAPTER 18 Introducing Algebra

The two algebra chapters should be done in their entirety only by above average ability groups, but all pupils can have some introduction to equations at this stage. We have suggested some convenient stopping places. Equations are dealt with again in Book 2A.

EXERCISE 18a Can be used for discussion.
(p. 264)

1. $x - 3 = 4$, 7	**5.** $2x = 8$, 4
2. $x + 1 = 3$, 2	**6.** $7x = 14$, 2
3. $3 + x = 9$, 6	**7.** $3x = 15$, 5
4. $x - 5 = 2$, 7	**8.** $6x = 24$, 4

EXERCISE 18b Useful to point out here that any letter can be used.
(p. 266)

1. 8	**5.** 4	**9.** 5	**13.** −2	**17.** −2
2. 9	**6.** 5	**10.** 7	**14.** −5	**18.** −4
3. 2	**7.** 6	**11.** 3	**15.** −1	
4. 7	**8.** 6	**12.** 1	**16.** −1	

19. 10	**23.** 9	**27.** 12
20. 3	**24.** 12	**28.** 3
21. 8	**25.** 5	**29.** 2
22. 10	**26.** 12	**30.** 9

EXERCISE 18c	**1.** 2	**3.** 3	**5.** 3
(p. 267)	**2.** 9	**4.** 13	**6.** 3

7. 7	**11.** 4	**15.** −1
8. −5	**12.** −3	**16.** 12
9. 0	**13.** 4	**17.** 10
10. 1	**14.** 8	**18.** 11

19. 10	**23.** 11	**27.** 9
20. 6	**24.** 16	**28.** 17
21. 11	**25.** 12	**29.** 5
22. 5	**26.** 10	**30.** 16
31. 23	**33.** 7	**35.** -7
32. 4	**34.** 9	**36.** 9
37. 4	**39.** 4	**41.** -2
38. 4	**40.** -2	**42.** 2

EXERCISE 18d (p. 268)

1. 2	**5.** 4	**9.** $1\frac{2}{5}$
2. 3	**6.** $2\frac{1}{4}$	**10.** 20
3. $2\frac{1}{2}$	**7.** $\frac{1}{3}$	**11.** 2
4. 3	**8.** 3	**12.** $\frac{1}{2}$
13. 6	**17.** $1\frac{4}{5}$	**21.** $\frac{3}{4}$
14. 1	**18.** $3\frac{1}{2}$	**22.** $1\frac{1}{5}$
15. $\frac{1}{6}$	**19.** 9	**23.** 5
16. 2	**20.** 2	**24.** $\frac{1}{7}$

EXERCISE 18e (p. 269)

1. 4	**5.** $1\frac{1}{5}$	**9.** $5\frac{1}{2}$
2. 12	**6.** 3	**10.** 13
3. 2	**7.** 8	**11.** 8
4. 1	**8.** 16	**12.** 16
13. 6	**17.** $\frac{2}{7}$	**21.** 7
14. $3\frac{1}{3}$	**18.** -1	**22.** 2
15. 5	**19.** $2\frac{2}{3}$	**23.** $1\frac{2}{3}$
16. -1	**20.** -5	**24.** 11
25. 0	**27.** 20	**29.** 30
26. 5	**28.** 30	**30.** $\frac{1}{5}$

EXERCISE 18f (p. 270)

1. 4	**8.** 5	**15.** 2
2. 3	**9.** -1	**16.** 3
3. 2	**10.** $2\frac{2}{3}$	**17.** 3
4. 6	**11.** 7	**18.** 0
5. 3	**12.** 5	**19.** -1
6. 0	**13.** 3	**20.** $1\frac{4}{5}$
7. 6	**14.** 5	**21.** 2

22. 2

23. $1\frac{2}{3}$

24. $-1\frac{4}{5}$

25. $\frac{1}{2}$

26. 4

27. -1

28. 0

29. 2

30. $3\frac{1}{3}$

31. $2\frac{3}{7}$

32. 3

33. $2\frac{1}{5}$

34. -6

35. $\frac{1}{3}$

36. 6

37. -1

38. $\frac{1}{4}$

39. 5

40. $\frac{6}{7}$

41. -3

42. -1

This is a convenient stopping place for average ability groups.

EXERCISE 18g Good questions to discuss with above average ability groups but only the
(p. 271) most able children should be allowed to work through these on their own.

1. $4x-8 = 20$, 7

2. $6x-12 = 30$, 7

3. $3x+6 = 21$, 5

4. $x+8 = 10$, 2

5. $3x+7 = 28$, 7

6. $2x+6 = 24$, 9

7. $2x+6 = 20$, 7

8. $2x+10 = 24$, 7

9. $3x-9 = 18$, 9

10. $2x+9 = 31$, 11 cm

EXERCISE 18h **1.** 4

(p. 273) **2.** 1

3. 3

4. 5

5. 7

6. $-\frac{3}{4}$

7. 6

8. 5

9. 7

10. 2

11. 1

12. 3

13. 1

14. 2

15. 3

16. 2

17. 2

18. 1

19. 6

20. -4

21. 3

22. -3

23. $1\frac{1}{3}$

24. 1

25. 1

26. 2

27. $\frac{1}{2}$

28. 2

29. 2

30. -2

31. 1

32. 0

33. 2

34. -2

35. $\frac{2}{3}$

36. 3

37. $-\frac{1}{2}$

38. $\frac{3}{10}$

39. -1

40. 3

41. $2\frac{1}{2}$

42. 1

43. $\frac{1}{4}$

44. 2

45. $-1\frac{2}{3}$

46. $1\frac{1}{3}$

EXERCISE 18i A lot of discussion is necessary to get over the idea of "a term of an
(p. 275) expression" and what is meant by "like terms" and "unlike terms".

1. $10x$

2. $4x$

3. $2x$

4. 2

5. $-2x$

6. $8y$

7. 7

8. -23

9. 1

10. 0

EXERCISE 18j
(p. 275)

1. $7x+7$
2. $5x+5$
3. $4x-5$

4. $5c-2a$
5. $8x-2y$
6. $8x+8y$

7. $8x+2y$
8. $4x+8y$
9. $8x+3$
10. $8x-8$
11. $3x-12$

12. $3y-x$
13. $-6x-6y$
14. $1-4x$
15. $7-5x$
16. $3-2x$

17. $10x-2y$
18. $11x-9y$
19. $15x$

20. $4x-7y+4z$
21. $9x+y-11$
22. -1

EXERCISE 18k
(p. 276)

1. 1
2. 1
3. 4
4. $1\frac{6}{7}$
5. 3

6. 6
7. 2
8. $4\frac{1}{2}$
9. 2
10. $-1\frac{1}{5}$

11. $\frac{1}{2}$
12. 2
13. $1\frac{2}{3}$

14. -6
15. 2
16. -1

17. 3
18. -6

19. $\frac{2}{3}$
20. 2

21. 1
22. 7
23. 2
24. 5
25. 1

26. 2
27. $-\frac{5}{8}$
28. -3
29. $\frac{1}{2}$
30. 10

EXERCISE 18l
(p. 277)

1. $\frac{2}{3}$
2. $x+4=10;\ 6$

3. 2
4. -1

5. $9x-y$
6. $1\frac{1}{3}$

EXERCISE 18m
(p. 277)

1. 2
2. $7c$

3. $1\frac{1}{2}$
4. 4

5. $4\frac{1}{3}$
6. $6a+1$

EXERCISE 18n
(p. 277)

1. $5\frac{1}{2}$
2. 0

3. 2
4. 0

5. $14-x=8+x;\ 3$
6. $3b$

EXERCISE 18p
(p. 278)

1. 4
2. $-x$

3. $-\frac{2}{5}$
4. 2

5. $2a+5c-d$
6. -2

CHAPTER 19 Volume

Calculators should be used for most numerical work in this chapter.

EXERCISE 19a
(p. 280)

1. 48 cm³	**7.** 24 m³	**13.** 64 cm³	**19.** 512 km³
2. 1600 mm³	**8.** 160 m³	**14.** 125 cm³	**20.** $3\frac{3}{8}$ km³
3. 5400 mm³	**9.** 12 cm³	**15.** 8 m³	**21.** 39.304 m³
4. 16 mm³	**10.** 7.2 cm³	**16.** $\frac{1}{8}$ cm³	
5. 31.72 m³	**11.** 4.32 m³	**17.** 15.625 cm³	
6. 10.5 cm³	**12.** 0.756 m³	**18.** 27 km³	

EXERCISE 19b
(p. 281)

1. 8   **2.** 6   **3.** 8   **4.** 12   **5.** 64
6. a) 128   b) 16   c) 2

The remainder of this chapter is suitable only for above average ability groups, except for the first few problems in Exercise 19f.

EXERCISE 19c
(p. 283)

1. 8000 mm³	**3.** 6 200 mm³	**5.** 92 000 000 mm³
2. 14 000 mm³	**4.** 430 mm³	**6.** 40 mm³
7. 3 000 000 cm³	**9.** 420 000 cm³	**11.** 0.022 cm³
8. 2 500 000 cm³	**10.** 6 300 cm³	**12.** 0.731 cm³

EXERCISE 19d
(p. 284)

1. 2500 cm³	**3.** 540 cm³	**5.** 35 000 cm³
2. 1760 cm³	**4.** 7.5 cm³	**6.** 28 cm³
7. 7 litres	**8.** 4 litres	**9.** 24 litres
10. 5000 litres	**11.** 12 000 litres	**12.** 4600 litres

EXERCISE 19e
(p. 284)

1. 30 cm³	**6.** 40 000 cm³
2. 2 m³	**7.** 28 cm³
3. 800 cm³	**8.** 8 m³
4. 600 cm³	**9.** 17.5 cm³
5. 5760 mm³	**10.** 180 cm³

EXERCISE 19f The first three problems are suitable for everybody to try.
(p. 285)

1. 60 m³	**4.** 125	**7.** 60	**10.** 1600
2. 7776 cm³	**5.** 48	**8.** 9000	
3. 6480 m³	**6.** 300 m³; 300 000	**9.** 64	

EXERCISE 19g
(p. 287)

1. a) 3 200 000 cm³   b) 3 200 000 000 mm³
2. 1600 cm³
3. 64 cm³
4. 50 000 cm³
5. 13 500 mm³

EXERCISE 19h   **1.** a) 8000 mm³   b) 0.000 008 m³
(p. 287)   **2.** 3.5 litres
                    3. 300 cm³
                    4. 0.512 cm³
                    5. 120 000 cm³

EXERCISE 19i   **1.** a) 9000 cm³   b) 9 000 000 mm³
(p. 287)   **2.** 440 cm³
                    3. 216 cm³
                    4. 288 cm³
                    5. 2400 litres

EXERCISE 19j   **1.** 0.0009 m³
(p. 287)   **2.** 10.8 litres
                    3. 75 litres
                    4. 8 cm³
                    5. 1.2 m³

EXERCISE 19k   **1.** a) no   b) no
(p. 288)   **2.** Yes, measurements needed. Lengths on the drawing are not correct.
                   3. no

EXERCISE 19l   **1** and **2.**   lines are the correct length
(p. 289)   **3.** a) lines are the correct length   c) no
                         d) one vertex is hidden behind another
                     4. a) and b) lines are the correct length

EXERCISE 19m   **2.** a) (i) 2   (ii) 2   (iii) 4 cm by 3 cm
(p. 291)   b) e.g.

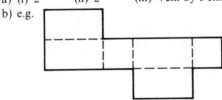

            3. a) 6
                 b) two faces 1 cm by 4 cm, two 2 cm by 1 cm, two 4 cm by 2 cm
            4. b) IJ   c) K and G
            5. a) IH   b) B and D
            6.

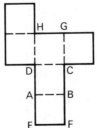

            7. There are a large number of arrangements of six squares and of these, 11 will
                 make cubes. (Count reflections as the same.)

CHAPTER 20 Vectors ──────────

This unit is optional. It can be done later (it is repeated with different exercises in Book 3) or omitted completely. If a brief introduction is thought appropriate, Exercise 20a and Exercise 20b form a good start.

Some pupils may suggest the need to state a time in the initial paragraph (p. 294); this can be dealt with if it arises but need not be introduced otherwise.

EXERCISE 20a **1.** scalar **4.** scalar
(p. 294) **2.** vector **5.** vector
  3. scalar

EXERCISE 20b **1.** $\binom{3}{2}$ **4.** $\binom{-2}{2}$ **7.** $g = \binom{5}{0}$ $h = \binom{-4}{0}$ $i = \binom{6}{2}$
(p. 295)
  2. $\binom{4}{1}$ **5.** $\binom{-3}{4}$ $j = \binom{-6}{7}$ $k = \binom{-6}{-2}$ $l = \binom{3}{-1}$
  3. $\binom{4}{0}$ **6.** $\binom{-5}{-3}$ $m = \binom{0}{-4}$ $n = \binom{4}{2}$

EXERCISE 20c **1.** $(7,4)$ **4.** $(1,-5)$ **7.** $(-1,0)$ **10.** $(7,-4)$
(p. 297) **2.** $(1,-2)$ **5.** $(8,1)$ **8.** $(-9,-8)$ **11.** $(-9,-1)$
  3. $(-3,7)$ **6.** $(8,0)$ **9.** $(2,0)$ **12.** $(-7,-3)$

  13. $(-6,-1)$ **18.** $(1,5)$
  14. $(-2,-3)$ **19.** $(-7,4)$
  15. $(3,-2)$ **20.** $(-1,-10)$
  16. $(-2,-3)$ **21.** $(-6,-6)$
  17. $(1,-3)$ **22.** $(-1,10)$

EXERCISE 20d **1.** $\binom{6}{2}$ **6.** $\binom{2}{-2}$
(p. 299)
  2. $\binom{5}{-1}$ **7.** $\binom{-2}{-2}$
  3. $\binom{-6}{-1}$ **8.** $\binom{-4}{-5}$
  4. $\binom{6}{5}$ **9.** $\binom{0}{-12}$
  5. $\binom{-5}{-6}$ **10.** $\binom{2}{8}$

EXERCISE 20e
(p. 301)

1. a) $b = 2a$ b) $c = -a$ c) $d = 3a$ d) $e = a$ e) $b = 2e$ f) $d = -3c$

2. $a = \begin{pmatrix} 4 \\ -2 \end{pmatrix}$ $b = \begin{pmatrix} -2 \\ -3 \end{pmatrix}$ $c = \begin{pmatrix} -4 \\ -6 \end{pmatrix}$ $d = \begin{pmatrix} 2 \\ 3 \end{pmatrix}$ $e = \begin{pmatrix} 8 \\ -4 \end{pmatrix}$ $f = \begin{pmatrix} -4 \\ 2 \end{pmatrix}$

$g = \begin{pmatrix} 6 \\ 9 \end{pmatrix}$ $h = \begin{pmatrix} -8 \\ 4 \end{pmatrix}$

$e = 2a$, $f = -a$, $h = -2a$, $c = 2b$, $d = -b$,
$g = -3b$, $h = -e$, $g = 3d$, $h = 2f$, . . .

3. $\begin{pmatrix} 8 \\ 12 \end{pmatrix}, \begin{pmatrix} -4 \\ -6 \end{pmatrix}, \begin{pmatrix} 2 \\ 3 \end{pmatrix}$

4. $\begin{pmatrix} 2 \\ -4 \end{pmatrix}, \begin{pmatrix} -4 \\ 8 \end{pmatrix}, \begin{pmatrix} 4 \\ -8 \end{pmatrix}$

5. $\begin{pmatrix} 10 \\ -8 \end{pmatrix}, \begin{pmatrix} -5 \\ 4 \end{pmatrix}, \begin{pmatrix} 15 \\ -12 \end{pmatrix}$

6. $\begin{pmatrix} 3 \\ 6 \end{pmatrix}, \begin{pmatrix} -6 \\ -12 \end{pmatrix}, \begin{pmatrix} 6 \\ 12 \end{pmatrix}$

7. $\begin{pmatrix} 10 \\ 2 \end{pmatrix}, \begin{pmatrix} -5 \\ -1 \end{pmatrix}, \begin{pmatrix} 15 \\ 3 \end{pmatrix}, \begin{pmatrix} -20 \\ -4 \end{pmatrix}$

8. $\begin{pmatrix} -6 \\ 0 \end{pmatrix}, \begin{pmatrix} 4 \\ 0 \end{pmatrix}, \begin{pmatrix} -10 \\ 0 \end{pmatrix}, \begin{pmatrix} 8 \\ 0 \end{pmatrix}$

9. $\begin{pmatrix} -6 \\ 4 \end{pmatrix}, \begin{pmatrix} 18 \\ -12 \end{pmatrix}, \begin{pmatrix} 3 \\ -2 \end{pmatrix}, \begin{pmatrix} -12 \\ 8 \end{pmatrix}$

10. $\begin{pmatrix} -18 \\ -60 \end{pmatrix}, \begin{pmatrix} 24 \\ 80 \end{pmatrix}, \begin{pmatrix} -3 \\ -10 \end{pmatrix}, \begin{pmatrix} 30 \\ 100 \end{pmatrix}$

EXERCISE 20f
(p. 303)

1. $\begin{pmatrix} 7 \\ -1 \end{pmatrix}$

2. $\begin{pmatrix} -8 \\ 2 \end{pmatrix}$

3. $\begin{pmatrix} 7 \\ -4 \end{pmatrix}$

4. $\begin{pmatrix} 2 \\ 6 \end{pmatrix}$

5. $\begin{pmatrix} 10 \\ 0 \end{pmatrix}$

6. $\begin{pmatrix} 4 \\ 3 \end{pmatrix}$

7. $\begin{pmatrix} -6 \\ -6 \end{pmatrix}$

8. $\begin{pmatrix} 3 \\ 6 \end{pmatrix}$

9. $\begin{pmatrix} 7 \\ 8 \end{pmatrix}$

10. $\begin{pmatrix} 6 \\ -4 \end{pmatrix}$

11. $\begin{pmatrix} 6 \\ 9 \end{pmatrix}$

12. $\begin{pmatrix} 7 \\ 11 \end{pmatrix}$

13. $\begin{pmatrix} 7 \\ 10 \end{pmatrix}$

14. $\begin{pmatrix} 10 \\ 0 \end{pmatrix}$

15. $\begin{pmatrix} -1 \\ 11 \end{pmatrix}$

16. $\begin{pmatrix} -2 \\ 10 \end{pmatrix}$

17. $\begin{pmatrix} -2 \\ -4 \end{pmatrix}$

18. $\begin{pmatrix} -5 \\ -2 \end{pmatrix}$

19. $\begin{pmatrix} -8 \\ 5 \end{pmatrix}$

20. $\begin{pmatrix} 0 \\ 0 \end{pmatrix}$

EXERCISE 20g
(p. 306)

1. a) $\begin{pmatrix} 7 \\ 5 \end{pmatrix}$ b) $\begin{pmatrix} 7 \\ 5 \end{pmatrix}$ c) $\begin{pmatrix} 8 \\ 6 \end{pmatrix}$ d) $\begin{pmatrix} 8 \\ 6 \end{pmatrix}$ e) $\begin{pmatrix} 4 \\ 6 \end{pmatrix}$ f) $\begin{pmatrix} 6 \\ 9 \end{pmatrix}$ g) $\begin{pmatrix} 10 \\ 9 \end{pmatrix}$ h) $\begin{pmatrix} 10 \\ 9 \end{pmatrix}$

2. a) $\begin{pmatrix} 3 \\ 2 \end{pmatrix}$ b) $\begin{pmatrix} 3 \\ 2 \end{pmatrix}$ c) $\begin{pmatrix} 0 \\ -5 \end{pmatrix}$ d) $\begin{pmatrix} 0 \\ -5 \end{pmatrix}$ e) $\begin{pmatrix} -6 \\ 12 \end{pmatrix}$ f) $\begin{pmatrix} -20 \\ -12 \end{pmatrix}$

3. a) $\begin{pmatrix} 5 \\ 10 \end{pmatrix}$ b) $\begin{pmatrix} 18 \\ 24 \end{pmatrix}$ c) $\begin{pmatrix} 12 \\ 24 \end{pmatrix}$

4. a) $\begin{pmatrix} -19 \\ -1 \end{pmatrix}$ b) $\begin{pmatrix} 4 \\ -11 \end{pmatrix}$

EXERCISE 20h **1.** $\begin{pmatrix} 5 \\ 3 \end{pmatrix}$ **3.** $\begin{pmatrix} 2 \\ 4 \end{pmatrix}$
(p. 307)

2. $\begin{pmatrix} 0 \\ 6 \end{pmatrix}$ **4.** $\begin{pmatrix} -5 \\ 1 \end{pmatrix}$

5. $\begin{pmatrix} 2 \\ 1 \end{pmatrix}$ **9.** $\begin{pmatrix} -3 \\ -2 \end{pmatrix}$ **13.** $\begin{pmatrix} 5 \\ 10 \end{pmatrix}$ **16.** $\begin{pmatrix} 2 \\ 3 \end{pmatrix}$

6. $\begin{pmatrix} 3 \\ 2 \end{pmatrix}$ **10.** $\begin{pmatrix} -7 \\ 3 \end{pmatrix}$ **14.** $\begin{pmatrix} 4 \\ -5 \end{pmatrix}$ **17.** $\begin{pmatrix} -3 \\ 11 \end{pmatrix}$

7. $\begin{pmatrix} 11 \\ 9 \end{pmatrix}$ **11.** $\begin{pmatrix} 2 \\ 4 \end{pmatrix}$ **15.** $\begin{pmatrix} 4 \\ -1 \end{pmatrix}$ **18.** $\begin{pmatrix} -11 \\ 7 \end{pmatrix}$

8. $\begin{pmatrix} 5 \\ 8 \end{pmatrix}$ **12.** $\begin{pmatrix} 1 \\ -1 \end{pmatrix}$

19. a) $\begin{pmatrix} 1 \\ 2 \end{pmatrix}$ b) $\begin{pmatrix} -1 \\ -2 \end{pmatrix}$

20. a) $\begin{pmatrix} -6 \\ -4 \end{pmatrix}$ b) $\begin{pmatrix} -3 \\ -3 \end{pmatrix}$ c) $\begin{pmatrix} 3 \\ 3 \end{pmatrix}$

21. a) $\begin{pmatrix} 8 \\ 2 \end{pmatrix}$ b) $\begin{pmatrix} 9 \\ 19 \end{pmatrix}$ c) $\begin{pmatrix} 0 \\ -22 \end{pmatrix}$ d) $\begin{pmatrix} 10 \\ 11 \end{pmatrix}$ e) $\begin{pmatrix} 0 \\ 3 \end{pmatrix}$

22. a) $\begin{pmatrix} -3 \\ 18 \end{pmatrix}$ b) $\begin{pmatrix} -3 \\ 0 \end{pmatrix}$ c) $\begin{pmatrix} 3 \\ 8 \end{pmatrix}$ d) $\begin{pmatrix} 0 \\ -23 \end{pmatrix}$ e) $\begin{pmatrix} -4 \\ 22 \end{pmatrix}$

23. a) $\begin{pmatrix} 5 \\ -10 \end{pmatrix}$ b) $\begin{pmatrix} -17 \\ 14 \end{pmatrix}$ c) $\begin{pmatrix} 20 \\ -14 \end{pmatrix}$

CHAPTER 21 More Algebra

This work should be done only with above average ability children and even then it can be left until later. The work in this chapter is repeated in Book 2A.

EXERCISE 21a **1.** $2x+2$ **5.** $8+10x$ **9.** $18-12x$
(p. 309)   **2.** $9x-6$ **6.** $12+10a$ **10.** $5x-5$
          3. $5x+30$ **7.** $5a+5b$ **11.** $14-7x$
          4. $12x-12$ **8.** $16x-12$ **12.** $24-16x$

EXERCISE 21b **1.** $6x+4$ **6.** $6x-15$ **11.** $-3x-8$ **16.** $6a-6$
(p. 309)   **2.** $10x+18$ **7.** $5x+23$ **12.** $-15-4x$ **17.** $2-12x$
          3. $3x+7$ **8.** $17x-23$ **13.** $6c-2$ **18.** $38-10w$
          4. $14x-18$ **9.** $5x+5$ **14.** $x-8$ **19.** $-3y-12$
          5. $4x+17$ **10.** $3x+3$ **15.** $7-8x$ **20.** $2-15z$

Multiplication of directed numbers: can be introduced in many ways. When this work is done with average ability children they will probably benefit from a more practical approach.

EXERCISE 21c
(p. 311)

1. -15	**5.** -42	**9.** -5
2. -8	**6.** $+12$	**10.** $+18$
3. $+14$	**7.** -18	**11.** $+27$
4. $+4$	**8.** $+16$	**12.** -16

13. -35	**17.** -24	**21.** -6
14. $+24$	**18.** $+8$	**22.** $+15$
15. -15	**19.** $+3$	**23.** -18
16. -45	**20.** -8	**24.** $+20$

25. -24	**27.** $+45$	**29.** -28
26. -24	**28.** -20	**30.** $+36$

EXERCISE 21d
(p. 312)

1. $-6x+30$	**6.** $-7x-28$
2. $-15c-15$	**7.** $-6d+6$
3. $-10e+6$	**8.** $-8-4x$
4. $-3x+4$	**9.** $-14+21x$
5. $-16+40x$	**10.** $-4+5x$

11. $12x+36$	**16.** $-3x-2$	**21.** $24+30x$	**26.** $6x+4y+2$
12. $10+15x$	**17.** $16-24x$	**22.** $-24-30x$	**27.** $-25-10x$
13. $6x-18$	**18.** $-6y+12x$	**23.** $24-30x$	**28.** $4x-4y$
14. $-14-7x$	**19.** $20x-5$	**24.** $-24+30x$	**29.** $-4c+5$
15. $-6x+2$	**20.** $-5+20x$	**25.** $-5a-5b$	**30.** $18x-9$

EXERCISE 21e
(p. 313)

1. $25x+12$	**6.** $13-8g$
2. $27-6c$	**7.** $x-2$
3. $14m-20$	**8.** $4f+12$
4. $3-6x$	**9.** $4s-3$
5. $6x-4$	**10.** $19x-3$

11. $17x-1$	**16.** $12x-14$	**21.** $14x+11$	**26.** $11x+7$
12. $9x-18$	**17.** $4x-12$	**22.** $-6x-19$	**27.** $-7-15x$
13. $9x+1$	**18.** $9x+19$	**23.** $14x-19$	**28.** $2x+21$
14. $15-5x$	**19.** $x-21$	**24.** $-6x+11$	**29.** $2x+15$
15. $12x+8$	**20.** $31x-11$	**25.** $15x-9$	**30.** $5x-2$

EXERCISE 21f
(p. 314)

1. 2	**6.** 2	**11.** $\frac{2}{3}$	**16.** 2
2. 0	**7.** 5	**12.** 4	**17.** 2
3. $1\frac{3}{8}$	**8.** 3	**13.** 0	**18.** $\frac{1}{5}$
4. 3	**9.** -3	**14.** 4	**19.** -1
5. 1	**10.** 5	**15.** $-3\frac{1}{2}$	**20.** $\frac{4}{5}$

21. 2	**26.** 2
22. 1	**27.** 5
23. -2	**28.** 1
24. 3	**29.** $3\frac{1}{4}$
25. -2	**30.** 2

EXERCISE 21g Should be used for discussion. Only the most able pupils should be allowed to
(p. 315)   work on their own.

1. 11	**5.** 22 p	**9.** 18 p	**13.** 4
2. 6	**6.** 16	**10.** 80°	
3. 9 cm	**7.** 20 p	**11.** 6	
4. 12	**8.** 4	**12.** 45°	

The remainder of this chapter can be omitted. The work is repeated in later
books.

EXERCISE 21h
(p. 317)

1. z^3	**7.** $a \times a \times a$	**13.** $2a$	**19.** $3 \times z \times z$
2. a^2	**8.** $x \times x \times x \times x$	**14.** $4x^2$	**20.** $2 \times a \times b \times c$
3. b^5	**9.** $b \times b$	**15.** $12a$	**21.** $4 \times z \times y \times y$
4. y^5	**10.** $a \times a \times a \times a \times a$	**16.** a^2b	**22.** $6 \times a \times a \times b$
5. s^3	**11.** $x \times x \times x \times x \times x \times x \times x$	**17.** $15xz^2$	**23.** $2 \times x \times x \times x$
6. z^6	**12.** $z \times z \times z \times z$	**18.** $5a^2b^2$	**24.** $3 \times a \times a \times a \times a \times b \times b$

25. $6xz$	**31.** z^4	**37.** y^2z^2
26. $6x^3$	**32.** $6z^2$	**38.** $10xyz$
27. $12a^2$	**33.** $24x^2$	**39.** a^7
28. $6a^3$	**34.** $16x$	**40.** $8x^4$
29. $2a^2bc$	**35.** $4s^3$	**41.** $axyz$
30. $24x^2y$	**36.** x^6	**42.** s^7

EXERCISE 21i
(p. 318)

1. 2	**5.** $\dfrac{3ab}{10}$	**9.** $\dfrac{c^2}{10}$	**13.** $\frac{2}{5}$	**17.** 4
2. $\frac{22}{5}$ or $4\frac{2}{5}$	**6.** $\frac{4}{3}$ or $1\frac{1}{3}$	**10.** 6	**14.** $\frac{7}{6}$ or $1\frac{1}{6}$	**18.** $\frac{2}{5}$
3. $\frac{5}{8}$	**7.** 3	**11.** $\dfrac{x^2}{4}$	**15.** $\frac{9}{7}$ or $1\frac{2}{7}$	**19.** $\dfrac{3c}{2y}$
4. $\dfrac{z^2}{6}$	**8.** $\dfrac{y^2}{24}$	**12.** 1	**16.** 2	**20.** $\dfrac{3}{10z}$

21. $\dfrac{r^2}{24}$	**25.** $\dfrac{x}{4}$	**29.** $\dfrac{ay}{4}$
22. $\dfrac{5z}{2}$	**26.** $\frac{7}{4}$ or $1\frac{3}{4}$	**30.** $\dfrac{y}{2x}$
23. $\dfrac{2}{3a}$	**27.** $\dfrac{20}{3b}$	**31.** $\dfrac{4}{b}$
24. 1	**28.** 1	**32.** $\dfrac{2x}{3y}$

EXERCISE 21j
(p. 320)

1. $x = 5$	**5.** $4 \times a \times a$
2. $4x - 11$	**6.** $x = 1\frac{1}{3}$
3. 13	**7.** $2x - 1$
4. $x = -4$	**8.** $x = 0$

EXERCISE 21k **1.** $x = -\frac{1}{2}$
(p. 320)   **2.** $-2x + 15$
                3. 12
                4. $60abc$

5. $x = 12$
6. 1
7. $5x + 6y$
8. $x = 3$

EXERCISE 21l **1.** $x = 2$
(p. 320)   **2.** a^6
                3. $6 + x + 12 = 4x;\ x = 6$
                4. $x = -3$

5. $4 - x$
6. $\frac{4}{5}$
7. $6x + 4$
8. $-2x + 10$

EXERCISE 21m **1.** $x = -3$
(p. 321)   **2.** $\frac{8}{5}$ or $1\frac{3}{5}$
                3. $x = 1$
                4. $x + x + 2 + 8 = 18;$ £4

5. $x \times x \times x \times x \times x \times x$
6. $4x - 6$
7. $5 - x$
8. We get $3 = 0$ which cannot be true
(This problem can be used to discuss ∞.)

CHAPTER 22 Statistics

EXERCISE 22a If a copy of the table is made then each item in the table can be crossed out once it
(p. 322)   has been "counted". The answers give the frequencies in each group.

    1. 7, 14, 17, 22, 12
    2. 4, 22, 18, 17, 7, 2, 1, 1
    3. 1, 2, 10, 15, 16, 20, 10, 6, 2

EXERCISE 22b **1.**
(p. 323)

	0	1	2	3	4
Frequency	7	15	4	3	1

    2.

	S	V	C	P
Frequency	14	7	7	8

    3.

	R	G	B	Y	P
Frequency	17	3	4	14	6

    4.

	22	23	24	25	26	27
Frequency	1	10	15	11	4	3

EXERCISE 22c **1.** a) 55   b) car
(p. 325)   **2.** a) 52
                3. a) plain salted
                4. a) red

EXERCISE 22d **1.** a) a cat   b) 8   c) 28
(p. 326)   **2.** a) 8   b) 1 mark, 1 pupil   c) 8   d) 28
                 3. a) 6   b) Art   c) French
                 4. a) Castle Hill   b) 10 000   c) Brotton, with 6500

EXERCISE 22e **1.** a) 47 b)

	1–3	4–6	7–9	10–12
Frequency	16	25	3	3

2.

	1–3	4–6	7–9	10–12
Frequency	34	34	8	3

3. a) 19   b) 11   c) 16   d) not possible to say
4. a) 153   b) 128   c) not possible to say
6. a) 12   b) 3
c) number given includes those who read five books

EXERCISE 22f **1.** a) seven car lengths   b) one car length per 10 mph
(p. 331)   c) weather, light, amount of traffic, type and straightness of road
                 2. a) all electric   b) all gas
                     c) solid fuel   d) gas
                 3. a) Margate   b) June
                     c) December in Aberdeen, January in Margate

EXERCISE 22g The answers are the angles for each slice.
(p. 334)
1. 96°, 132°, 60°, 42°, 30°   **7.** 96°, 120°, 36°, 72°, 36°
2. 128°, 152°, 48°, 24°, 8°   **8.** 108°, 180°, 40°, 18°, 14°
3. 303°, 3°, 30°, 24°   **9.** 72°, 13.5°, 85.5°, 94.5°, 54°, 40.5°
4. 84°, 204°, 48°, 24°   **10.** 62°, 82°, 82°, 21°, 10°, 103°
5. 144°, 48°, 80°, 88°   **11.** 223°, 40°, 54°, 36°, 7°
6. 140°, 70°, 70°, 80°   **12.** 35°, 116°, 128°, 58°, 23°

EXERCISE 22h **1.** a) business and professional   b) i) $\frac{1}{12}$ ii) $\frac{7}{36}$
(p. 337)   **2.** a) heating   b) a little less
                 3. a) i) $\frac{1}{8}$ ii) $\frac{1}{6}$ b) under 10 and 10–19

EXERCISE 22i **1.** a) 10, 14, 10, 22   b) danger   c) very effective (open to discussion)
(p. 338)   **2.** a) French   b) 18, 15, 11, 12, 16: total 72
                 c) this is not a good way to present the information because it is not clear how
                     many pupils part of a body represents (open to discussion).
                 3. a) consumption is rising each year
                     b) impression is given by the volume of the bottle which goes up more quickly
                         than the height of the bottle

EXERCISE 22j **1.** 6
(p. 340)   **2.** 25 p
           3. a) £40   b) £8   c) £8
           4. 10
           5. a) 5   b) 15   c) 33   d) 2.6
           6. 12
           7. 13.5 p   **8.** 7.2   **9.** 308.8 p   **10.** 329

EXERCISE 22k **1.** 40 cm
(p. 342)   **2.** 27 p
           3. a) 12 p   b) 0.4 kg   c) 10 mm d) £3.25
           4. a) 44 cm   b) 147.3 cm
           5. a) 12   b) 10.3
           6. a) 48 p   b) 25 p

CHAPTER 23 Decision Trees

EXERCISE 23a **1.**
(p. 344)

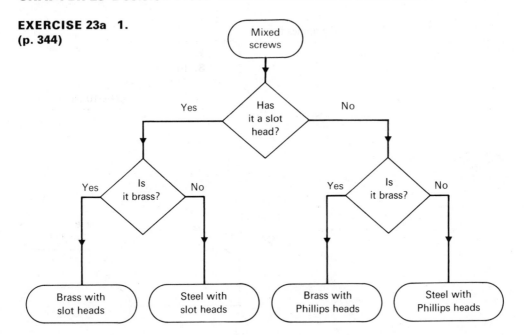

2. a)

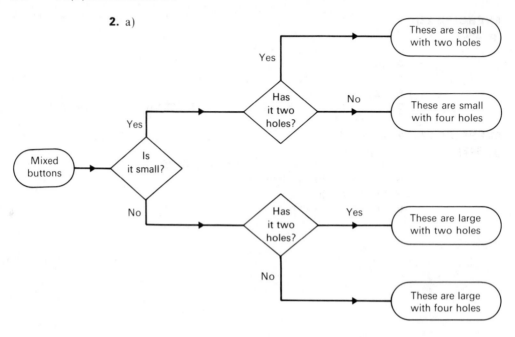

b)

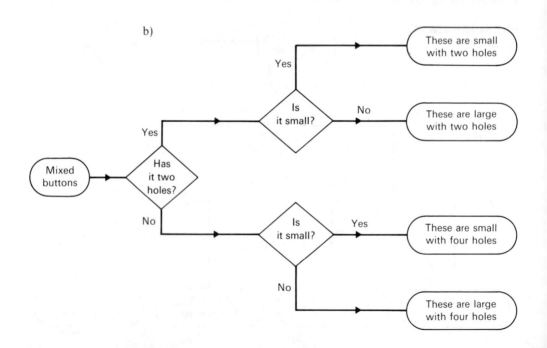

3. a) separate knives from forks first; separate stainless steel from silver-plated first

b) (i)

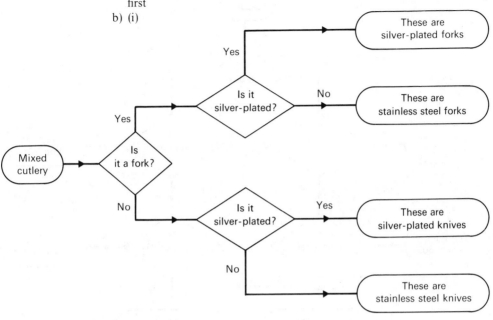

(ii)

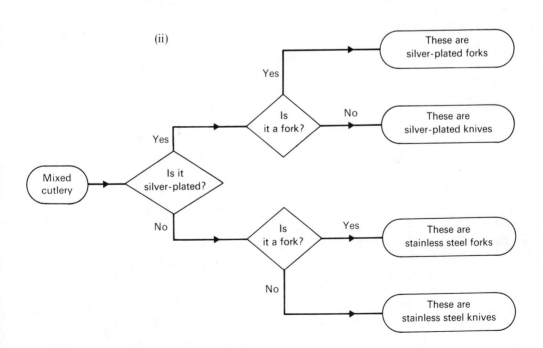

4.

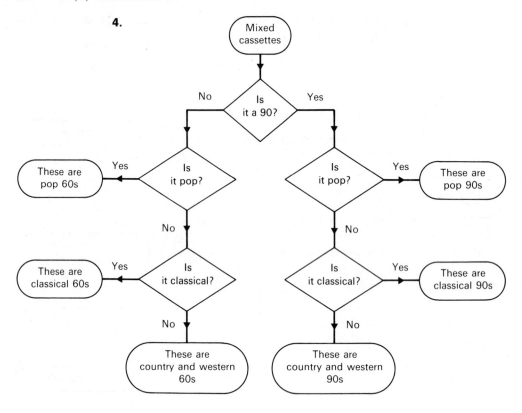

5. a) 6

    b) 3–4 inch goldfish; 5–6 inch goldfish; 3–4 inch orfe; 5–6 inch orfe; 3–4 inch rudd; 5–6 inch rudd.

c)

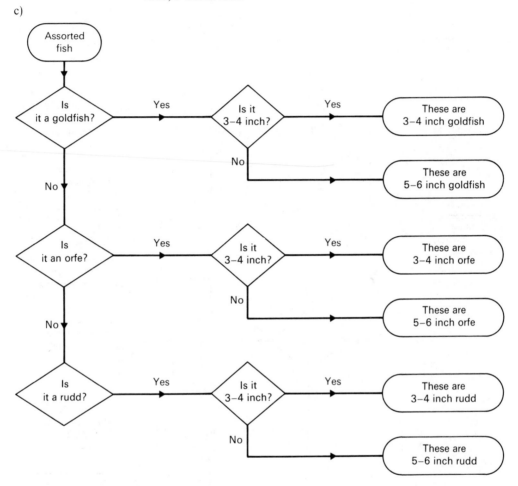

6.

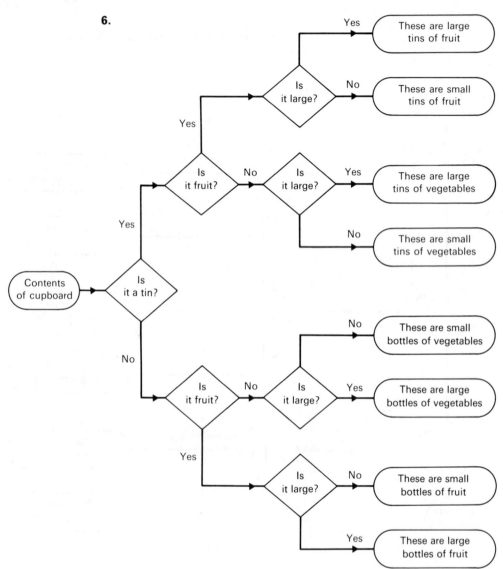

7. a)

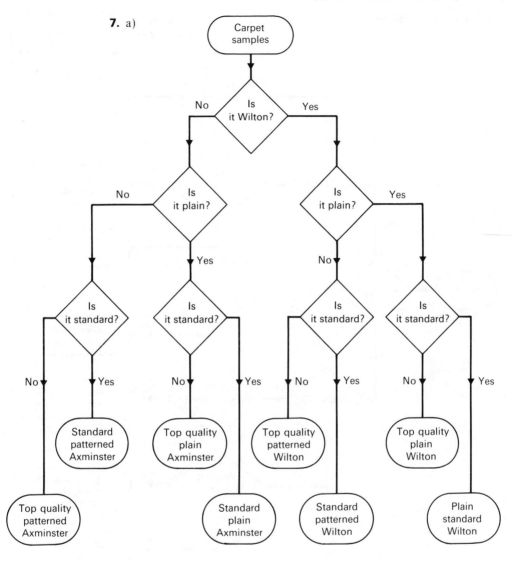

8. a) 8

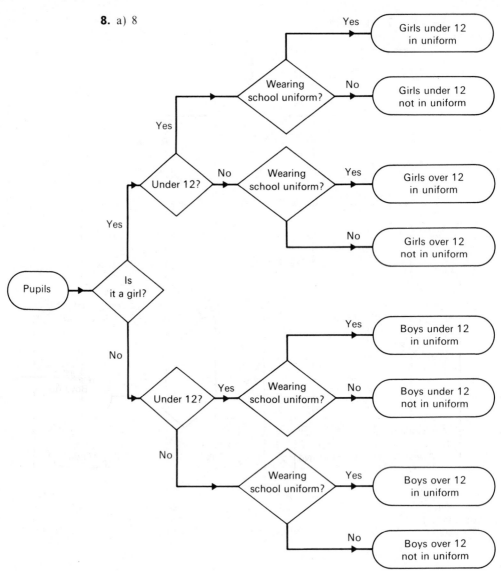

b)

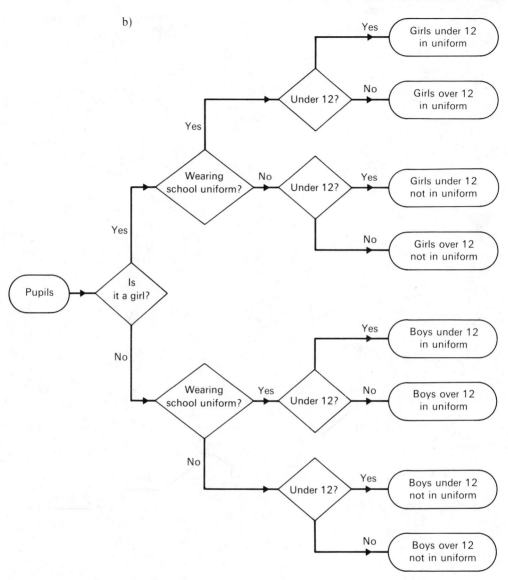

c) Yes